**Above.** *Tawny Owl in barrel nestbox (Photo A K Davies)*

**Left.** *Chimney for Tawny Owls (Photo J Mountford)*

**Below.** *Concrete tit box. (Photo C R du Feu)*

*An artificial Sand Martin nest site.*
**Above.** *Distant view.*
**Below.** *Close-up view.*
*(Photos R T Smith)*

# NESTBOXES

by

CHRIS DU FEU

British Trust for Ornithology
Field Guide Number 23

Cover design by Robert Gillmor

*Published by*
*The British Trust for Ornithology*
*National Centre for Ornithology*
*The Nunnery, Thetford, Norfolk, IP24 2PU*
*1985*
*Reprinted with additions and alterations 1989*
*Second edition 1993*

*du Feu, C.R. (1993). Nestboxes: BTO Guide 23*
*British Trust for Ornithology, Thetford. © BTO*
*ISBN 0-903793-29-6*

# CONTENTS

# INTRODUCTION

Garden nestboxes have been a source of pleasure and interest for many years, but now these and other artificial nest sites assume greater importance as a means of protecting birds from the pressures of our ways of life. These pressures come from industry, urban development, agricultural practices, dutch elm disease, the great storms of 1987 and 1990, loss of traditional habitat and interference from human leisure interests. Some pressures make life more difficult for the birds in general, others affect nesting sites in particular. The provision of nestboxes can mean the difference between the survival of a species and its loss from a particular area. Even some of our once common species are becoming not-so-common; nestboxes for them could provide the helping hand they need in an environment where holes and cavities are tidied up. There is almost no habitat where artificial nest sites are inappropriate. Even humble garden nestboxes are important, gardens now forming a major habitat in Britain, covering more land area than do nature reserves. In inner cities there are opportunities to encourage Swifts and Kestrels, not just House Sparrows or Starlings. In addition to their direct value for conservation, properly monitored nestboxes can provide a wealth of information vital for the understanding of basic bird biology and population ecology. They can also contribute to monitoring the overall 'health' of our environment and the birds in it. The chapter Inspection and Recording gives more details of some of the BTO's population monitoring schemes.

The definition of a nestbox taken in this book is very broad. It includes any artificial device constructed with the express purpose of attracting birds to nest. This includes rafts for wildfowl and terns, tunnels for Wheatears, Kingfishers and Sand Martins as well as conventional boxes for Robins, Wrens and Blue Tits. This book does not list all the artefacts which have been used by nesting birds - such things include narrow drain pipes for Great Tits, overcoat pockets in garden sheds for Robins, lorries and cars for Pied Wagtails and even a human skull for Wrens. Instead the book concentrates on good practical designs. A good design is one which has as many of the following attributes as possible. Birds must accept and use the box successfully and produce broods of healthy young. It must be secure from predators and weatherproof. It should be simple and cheap to construct and maintain, convenient to inspect and durable.

Dimensions of boxes need not be measured to the nearest millimetre. If birds were so selective that they took only nest sites of such precise dimensions then there would be insufficient natural sites, making life impossibly hard. Birds are opportunists and may take any of a wide range of nest sites. Our aim must be to ensure that the sites we provide are as suitable and safe as possible. There is no ideal design for a species because the requirements depend on local conditions such as climate, predators, competing species, materials available and the preferences of the population in the area. Nest site preferences differ from one area to another. In some parts, for example, Tawny Owls may use the chimney nestbox design exclusively whilst elsewhere they will only take a more conventional large hole entrance box. For these reasons this book is not dogmatic about the right design, but it does give general principles to be followed for success. There is still plenty of room for experimentation in nestbox design, siting and defence against predators.

There are many opportunities for large scale nestbox schemes. These may either use many assorted boxes in a small area such as a garden or local nature reserve, or more widely spread boxes of a single design aimed at attracting only a particular species or group. In all cases landowners' assistance will be vital and every effort must be made in keeping them in touch with events. Anecdotes and information about nesting success help stimulate interest. Bird ringers should pass on details of numbers ringed and of those found again. Some recorders produce annual newsletters to keep landowners and helpers informed and enthusiastic. The interest created leads to increased assistance and can turn a former persecutor into a keen conservationist. The tangible benefits of contacts with landowners include help with materials, transport and equipment like long ladders and rope. The intangible benefits to conservation are also great. People not directly involved are often most helpful in supplying materials once their interest has been aroused. Various organisations will provide help with nestbox schemes - these include local councils, industry and charities as well as the county naturalists' trusts. Schools can be involved too. With the current emphasis on project work in schools, well directed work can be of benefit to the birds as well as to the students. Nestboxes are fairly straightforward to produce and it is often possible to use local non-ornithological talent to make them. One county wildlife trust, for example, uses owl boxes produced by inmates at a local prison. Many nature reserves have sponsored nestbox schemes. This is a sound way of raising funds, providing bird nest sites and creating interest in bird life.

Nestboxes are not always used immediately after they have been put up. This has disappointed many a garden nestbox owner (a typical suburban Blue Tit territory might cover 10 or more gardens). Perseverance is essential. Birds will learn the nestbox habit and eventually local populations can become reliable box users. This learning process may take time. The prize for endurance must go to the Scottish Goldeneye nestbox team who waited 15 years for success, but now have established a secure British breeding population of these attractive ducks. If your box does not attract a Blue Tit to nest it is still not a wasted box. Birds will use boxes for roosting in during cold weather and can help them survive the harshest conditions - there are records of over 50 Wrens roosting in a single box. The box which provides a home for no wildlife whatsoever is exceptional. Bats, hedgehogs, mice, moths, bees, spiders, slugs and many others welcome a safe hiding place.

The book is split into two major sections - Designs and Species Notes. The design section does not give precise dimensions, but only general outlines to be adapted according to species and materials available. Species Notes gives particular details for each species and refers back to the design section. The two sections are preceded and followed by general instructions and other related matters. In the text, page references are given to diagrams where these are not on a facing page and in a few other places to add clarity. Detailed cutting diagrams for commonly used small boxes are included in the appendix, but it must be stressed that they are not the only sizes or designs of box that are suitable and that they require long, expensive wooden planks. There is also a cutting diagram for a Barn Owl box using a large plywood sheet.

This book will not be the last word on nestboxes. Like its predecessors it has depended on the many contributions from BTO members and others. The BTO welcomes further ideas, designs or knowledge to add to a future edition. Any ideas or additional information should be sent to the Nest Records Officer at the BTO.

# GENERAL INSTRUCTIONS

Any exceptions to the following instructions are detailed under Species Notes.

## DIMENSIONS

Apart from entrance hole sizes, dimensions are not critical for most boxes. In the following notes and under Species Notes the broad categories below are used to describe the size of boxes and height of mounting.

| Size | Base | Height | Mounting Height | |
|------|------|--------|-----------------|---|
| | (mm x mm) | (mm) | | |
| Very Small | 80 x 80 | 80 | Low | about waist to head height |
| Small | 100 x 100 | 150 | Medium | chest height to about 5 m. |
| Medium | 130 x 130 | 200 | High | around 5m. and above |
| Large | 200 x 200 | 450 | | |
| Very Large | 250 x 250 | 600 | | |

## MATERIALS AND TOOLS

Wood is the best material for making nestboxes, but can be expensive. For large scale construction of boxes it is better to obtain wood from sources such as scrap heaps belonging to timber merchants or sawmills. Many companies throw out pallets and packing cases. These provide very useful wood, although dismantling them efficiently takes practice and care. Second-hand timber such as old floorboards can be obtained cheaply but beware of nails. Coastal dwellers may be able to use driftwood including fish boxes or packing cases which are almost ready-made to use as nestboxes. Wood under 15mm thick may warp, will not provide enough insulation and will become waterlogged too easily. Almost any type of wood will do. Softwood is easier to work, hardwood longer lasting. Cedar is very long lasting, birch is not. Dimensions of nestboxes are generally not critical and it is easier, cheaper and more effective to make boxes according to wood available rather than to adhere slavishly to precise dimensions.

Other useful materials which may be obtained free include sawdust, oil drums, binder twine, car tyres, tractor inner tubes and various bits of piping. Local firms will often be very helpful with a nestbox project if they receive even minimal acknowledgement or publicity.

Materials other than wood have been used for nestboxes. However metal suffers from condensation and is a poor insulator. Boxes made completely from plastic will also suffer condensation, but those with at least some wood components have been found to be satisfactory. Some workers use recycled plastic board for roofs only. This has the advantage of being waterproof and durable and also keeps rain off the wooden parts of the box. Others use thick walled gas pipes for the body of the box with a wooden roof and floor. It is best to use more natural coloured plastics because bright colours will attract unwanted human attention. Manufactured interior boards such as chipboard are only suitable for boxes located under shelter e.g. Barn Owl or Swift boxes. Marine or exterior plywood (WBP) can be used in any situation. Both are very long lasting but expensive. Other materials such as sawdust/cement and papier-mâché are mentioned in connection with specific types of boxes. This list of materials is not exhaustive. Keen conservationists will often find sources of good, cheap or free, unconventional materials - use them.

For most small boxes only basic woodworking tools are needed. If you intend to make many boxes of different sizes it is worth buying an adjustable drill bit for a hand brace or an electric drill attachment with several different circular cutting blades. A most useful size of

# CONSTRUCTION FEATURES

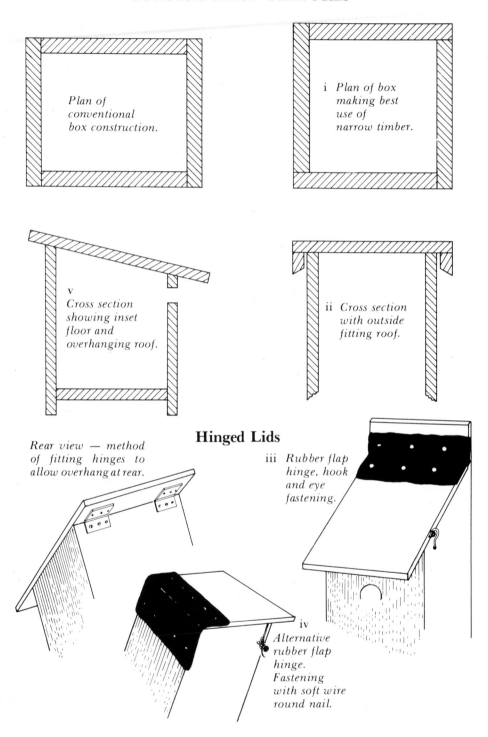

Plan of
conventional
box construction.

i  Plan of box
making best
use of
narrow timber.

v
Cross section
showing inset
floor and
overhanging roof.

ii  Cross section
with outside
fitting roof.

## Hinged Lids

Rear view — method
of fitting hinges to
allow overhang at rear.

iii  Rubber flap
hinge, hook
and eye
fastening.

iv
Alternative
rubber flap
hinge.
Fastening
with soft wire
round nail.

drill bit is 28mm ($1^1/_8$") which will make holes large enough for tits but too small for sparrows. This bit is the size used for cutting Yale lock holes in doors.

# CONSTRUCTION OF WOODEN BOXES

The plans in this and the Designs section do not give exact dimensions and should be modified according to materials available. The dimensions required for particular species are given under Species Notes.

Where possible the grain of wood should be vertical to help rain water drain quickly. Mount the floor just above the lowest point of the side panels to make water drip off the sides rather than seep into the end grain of the wooden base. Where possible avoid exposed horizontal end grain. If your woodworking is so good that the floor meets the walls in watertight joints, drill small drainage holes because any water which gets inside must be able to drain away. When two pieces of wood are to be joined along their length they may be tongued and grooved, rebated or joined with an inside lining piece to stop wind and rain entering.

Wood may be fixed with nails or screws. Nails are much easier and cheaper. In wetter parts of the country and damp situations it is essential to use galvanized nails or brass screws. Wire nails will rust within a very few years. Top and side joints should be sealed with waterproof glue in wet areas but never rely on glue alone for joints. Boxes need not have a symmetrical horizontal cross section - if very wide wood is not available, narrower wood arranged as shown (page 8i) is quite acceptable to the birds. When using plywood never screw or nail along laminations, only perpendicular to them.

Boxes should have a means of easy access for inspection and cleaning. Apart from the interest provided by observing the progress of a nest, boxes can provide valuable information (preferably to be submitted to the British Trust for Ornithology Nest Record Scheme - see Inspection and Recording). Access may be through a hinged or removable roof or through an opening front. The cheapest hinges are of old tyre inner tubes which also provide sealing from elements and are easy to fit. Hinges with any steel parts will soon rust. Brass hinges are excellent but expensive. Boxes with removable roofs are easier to inspect than those with hinged ones. This is important where many boxes are to be inspected regularly. Removable roofs also allow an overhang on all four sides. This helps to protect the box from sun and rain. Roofs with a flange around the rim (page 8ii) which fits over the top of the box, biscuit tin fashion, are the most waterproof. For extra rainproofing you can cover the roof with felt, vinolay or rubber from old inner tubes. Large boxes in particular will benefit from professional felting techniques - a blowlamp etc. Roofs may be fixed securely using hooks and eyes, loose fitting nails used as locating pins (page 10i 10ii 10iii) or by gravity (use a heavy stone) according to taste and circumstances. Simple catches can be made of three staples - two on the box, one on the lid (page 10iv) - and a locking nail or using wire wrapped round a nail (page 8iv). It is a matter of personal preference whether you use top or front opening boxes. Front openings allow a more waterproof roof, but can be more draughty lower down the box.

In general perches are a hazardous feature on all small and medium sized boxes and should not be fitted. They are not needed by birds (with some exceptions given under Species Notes) but do provide a foothold for predators.

Very large boxes can be reinforced with a jacket of wire netting. This will both hold the joints tightly and prevent warping. Such boxes are often difficult and expensive to make and difficult to erect. It is well worth spending extra time and money to ensure that they last as long as possible.

# CONSTRUCTION FEATURES

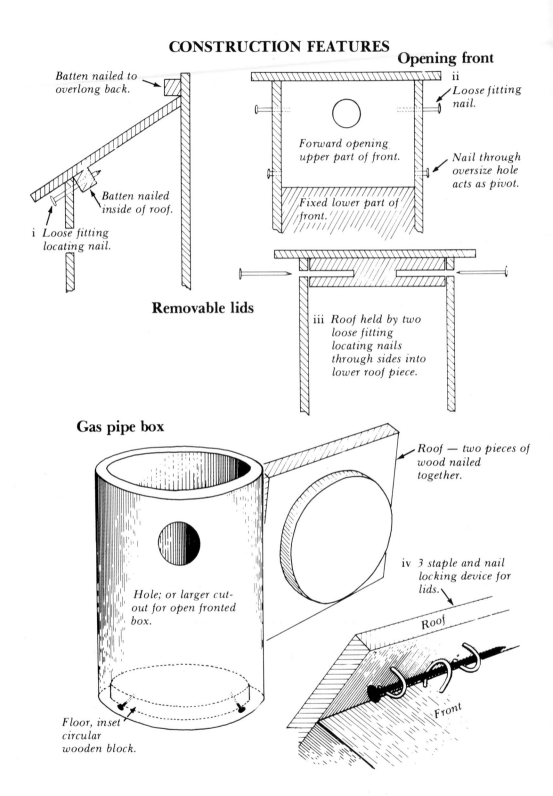

**Opening front**

Batten nailed to overlong back.

ii Loose fitting nail.

Forward opening upper part of front.

Nail through oversize hole acts as pivot.

Batten nailed inside of roof.

Fixed lower part of front.

i Loose fitting locating nail.

**Removable lids**

iii Roof held by two loose fitting locating nails through sides into lower roof piece.

**Gas pipe box**

Roof — two pieces of wood nailed together.

iv 3 staple and nail locking device for lids.

Hole; or larger cut-out for open fronted box.

Roof

Front

Floor, inset circular wooden block.

# CONSTRUCTION OF OTHER BOXES.

## Sawdust/Cement

Many designs of boxes can be made with this mixture. It has the advantages of being fairly predator-proof and of being easy for use in mass production. The disadvantages include the potential difficulty of making the initial mould. The sawdust/cement mixture can be sawn, screwed or nailed once it has set and hardened although initial attempts with these boxes often end in a heap of fragments. The material is suitable for House Martin and Swallow boxes, free hanging tit boxes and many other designs. This material is widely used on the continent for factory, rather than home, produced boxes. Production of these boxes requires practice.

Method. Make a mould from wood or plastic. Soak fine sawdust overnight in a solution containing a wetting agent (any not too frothy detergent). Squeeze surplus moisture out of the sawdust and allow it to dry. Mix the dried sawdust with fresh cement in the proportions 1:3½ by volume cement:sawdust. Add water to make a fairly wet mixture. The mould should be wetted with a strong soap or detergent solution. Pour the mixture into the mould, press down very firmly and allow to dry. Fittings (hooks, locking tabs etc.) to the box may be attached using a strong adhesive. Fittings should be of a rust-proof material. It is essential that the sawdust is thoroughly wetted and that the mixture is very firmly pressed into the mould. Failure to ensure these two details will make a porous box which cracks when exposed to frost - if not before! A hanging tit box with the lid held on by the weight of the box is illustrated (page 22i). Alternatively the box can be made with an opening front. Sawdust/cement boxes are commercially available from Germany. Some other German boxes are made from an asbestos/cement mixture called Eternit. It seems that these may suffer from high infestation by parasites.

## Fibreglass

Fibreglass can be used in a similar way to sawdust/cement. Its main disadvantage is that of cost but it has been used successfully for Kingfisher boxes. Mix some sawdust with the resin to give a roughened inner surface the the box.

## Built-in boxes

Many domestic, commercial and industrial buildings provide suitable sites for built-in boxes. The scope is great. For example some road bridges now incorporate built-in sites for Swallows and Swifts. It is easiest to install boxes during building, although this is not always convenient. Two methods are possible.

The first method involves having a box inside the building with access through a hole in the wall. Swift boxes are of this type. The same technique has been used with ground level entrances for Puffins. Such boxes are very useful for regular observations if fitted with a window and blackout. With indoor boxes it is important to ensure that they are as insect proof as possible, and that cleaning out is done thoroughly late each autumn with a vacuum cleaner. In order to prevent contamination with Salmonella, boxes which are placed inside barns and other such buildings used for storing food must not allow the birds to come into contact with the foodstuffs .

The second method is to have the nestbox as an integral part of a wall building block (page 12i). This may require concrete blocks precast in two sections. The lower section contains the nest bowl and the upper the entrance. The upper block should not be cemented in place to allow for inspection. These boxes are of particular value to urban birds and may be set in walls at any height. A 'box' for Spotted Flycatcher (or perhaps Pied Wagtail, Robin or even Black Redstart) consists of a missing brick in a wall, preferably with a very low retaining lip along the front edge (page 12ii).

# BUILT-IN BOXES
## Holes in walls

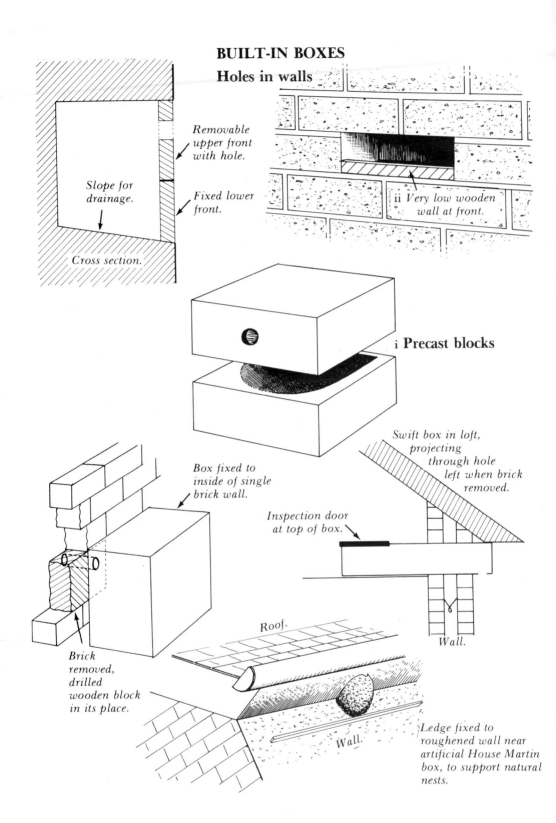

Removable upper front with hole.

Fixed lower front.

Slope for drainage.

Cross section.

ii *Very low wooden wall at front.*

i **Precast blocks**

Box fixed to inside of single brick wall.

Swift box in loft, projecting through hole left when brick removed.

Inspection door at top of box.

Brick removed, drilled wooden block in its place.

Roof.

Wall.

Wall.

Ledge fixed to roughened wall near artificial House Martin box, to support natural nests.

Several companies now produce ready made building blocks and tiles with integral nest chambers. ACO Ltd. make a polymerised concrete box which is exactly three brick courses high and half a brick wide. The removable top part of the front allows for inspection and cleaning, or it may just be left off to provide a site for Spotted Flycatchers or Robins. These boxes may also be mounted on existing walls rather than being built into new walls. It is hoped that these will become a common extra to new suburban and rural houses.

**Papier Mâché**

This material is suitable for House Martin boxes. In making a conventional mixture, use waterproof glue. Place the mixture around a Plaster of Paris or other suitable mould and allow to dry. Use galvanized metal fittings and put these in place whilst the mixture is being put over the mould. The dried box can be coated with mud coloured waterproof paint to aid durability. Boxes may also be made using strips of newspaper glued over a mould with waterproof glue in the manner that puppets are made in school. The stages in construction are illustrated (page 14).

**Rustic Boxes**

There is no evidence that these boxes are taken in preference to any other type (except by humans). Their disadvantages include difficulty of construction. Many garden centre rustic boxes (thatched roof, integral feeding table etc.) are of fundamentally bad design. Other faults include the perch, an over-large hole set too low down, a fixed roof not allowing cleaning and small size. There are two basic techniques for rustic boxes. The first involves boring a hole down through the centre of a log, then fitting base and roof. This is very time consuming, and often leads to unsatisfactory results with leaky joints. The second technique is to split a log longitudinally into four sectors and remove the apex of each sector, effectively removing the heartwood. Reassemble the four remaining pieces, binding them together tightly. These boxes are easier to make but even less weather proof than the former type. Birch, often used for these boxes because of its attractive bark, rots quickly. A good compromise is to use planks cut from the edge of logs with one flat and one rounded face. These are often thrown out by manufacturers and are easily obtainable.

**Plastic**

A variety of plastic designs is available. Many are ingenious or attractive but are of limited use to birds. Thin plastic offers little protection from the heat of the sun and is no protection against grey squirrels. Heavy reclaimed plastic has been used by some people for parts of boxes - either the roof or the sides. However other people report that such boxes have a lower take-up rate than wooden boxes and that the nests become wet with condensation. The Halo Company is field testing a double skinned plastic design which may be carried flat and assembled on site. This has clear advantages where many boxes need to be used - 100 or so wooden boxes in a remote wood are not easy for a single person to carry. Take great care to ensure they are sited out of the direct rays of the sun because they heat up so rapidly.

**Others**

Large boxes such as rafts or platforms in water will need a professional standard of work in order to endure severe environmental conditions, their own weight (including gravel etc.) and the weight of occupants including perhaps bird ringers. This work may involve welding in the case of steel girder framed types. No aspect of construction should be skimped as avian or human casualties may result.

# CONSTRUCTION OF PAPIER-MACHE BOXES

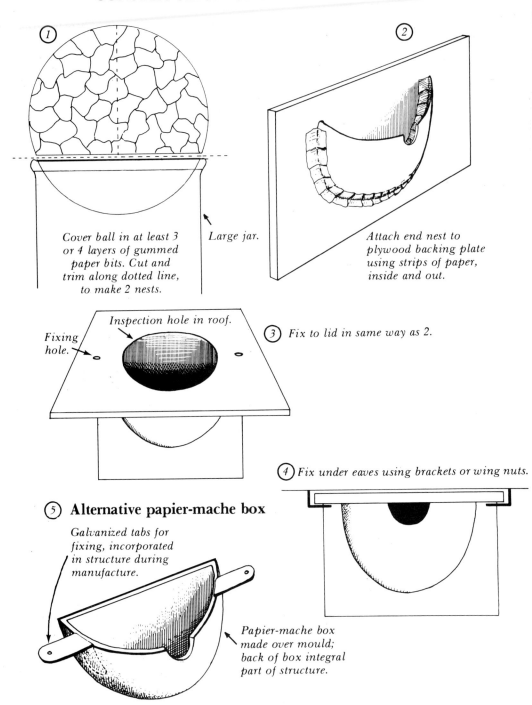

① Cover ball in at least 3 or 4 layers of gummed paper bits. Cut and trim along dotted line, to make 2 nests.

Large jar.

② Attach end nest to plywood backing plate using strips of paper, inside and out.

Inspection hole in roof.

Fixing hole.

③ Fix to lid in same way as 2.

④ Fix under eaves using brackets or wing nuts.

⑤ **Alternative papier-mache box**

Galvanized tabs for fixing, incorporated in structure during manufacture.

Papier-mache box made over mould; back of box integral part of structure.

# FIXING

There are many ways to fix boxes. Use the ones which suit you best. A horizontal (page 16i) or vertical (page 16ii) batten may be attached to the back of the box and then fixed to a tree or wall. The batten keeps the box away from the mounting surface and prevents water from running into the box. The batten must be fixed securely to the box. Use screws, safety nails or long nails bent over.

There is no absolutely reliable way of fixing boxes to living trees. If nails or pegs are used they may be gradually pushed out of the tree as it grows. Since the time of greatest growth is in the nesting season there is the danger that the box falls with a nest inside. Nailed boxes must be checked annually. Screws can be used and slackened off a little each year, but this also means annual attention. Nails or screws damage trees and should be avoided on timber with commercial value. Nylon, copper, aluminium, brass and hardwood nails can be obtained which will not damage the woodman's chain-saw (also preventing accidents to the woodman). Steel screws or nails must not be used as they rust quickly and become impossible to remove or adjust. If boxes are to be screwed to trees, select the hard wood ones because screws become very difficult to move in softer trees like sycamore. If you are putting up boxes on other people's property, ensure you have the landowner's agreement about the method of fixing to be used. Boxes may be nailed to trees provided that hardwood battens are used. Holes through the battens should be drilled to fit the nails snugly. Nails used should have flat and circular rather than oval or tapered heads. With this arrangement, as the trees grow, the nails will move out with the batten rather than being pulled through the batten. If you use this method, ensure nails are taken out when boxes are taken down. Do not use nails where there is any possibility of trees being used as commercial timber.

Boxes may be tied using wire (army surplus telephone cable is cheap), robust rubber bands or synthetic twine. Wire needs regular checking to ensure it does not constrict tree growth. Rubber bands (cut from large inner tubes) need checking to ensure they have not perished, but they do allow the tree to grow. Polypropylene binder twine has some elasticity and may be long lasting although some binder twine is now bio-degradable and does not last more than a year or two. Boxes may be loosely tied, the twine making an angle of 30° or so upwards from them. To allow for growth merely edge the box upwards a few centimetres a year. The twine will probably last as long as the box, is relatively cheap and easy to use. Like boxes secured by nails or screws, tied boxes need annual attention. Even twine can kill a tree by strangulation. Plastic covered extendable curtain wire allows the tree to grow, but it is expensive and only suitable for small boxes.

It is possible in some situations to wedge boxes firmly in tree forks without nailing or tying. Some large nesting platforms are probably best fixed in this way, resting on a horizontal fork and jammed into position. This method is illustrated under Chimney Boxes. Larger boxes for Kestrels, wildfowl or owls may be mounted on poles.

It is not essential to fix boxes rigidly (although most are), indeed boxes may hang freely attached only by a wire. This will help keep off predators, particularly if the wire is greasy or if it runs through a circular baffle plate, but such boxes may be more obvious to curious humans. Some workers have suspended boxes from small branches cut down to stumps a few centimetres in length. These boxes are inspected by lifting them down from the hook formed by the stump using a long pole. There is no reason (other than tradition) why boxes for small birds should not be made like miniature Chimney Boxes to simulate hollow boughs.

Large boxes will need heavier fixing gear. This can include pipe fixing brackets where boxes are to be attached to suitable posts or girders. Modern synthetic ropes can be used in places as they have the advantage of having some stretch in them. When fixing large boxes,

# FIXING BOXES

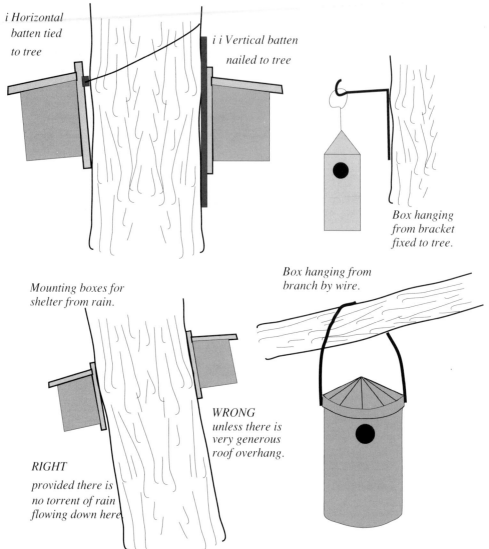

*i Horizontal batten tied to tree*

*i i Vertical batten nailed to tree*

*Box hanging from bracket fixed to tree.*

*Box hanging from branch by wire.*

*Mounting boxes for shelter from rain.*

*WRONG unless there is very generous roof overhang.*

*RIGHT provided there is no torrent of rain flowing down here*

block and tackle are useful. A team of at least two people should be employed - not only for ease of operation but also in case of accidents in remote places.

In places where boxes are to be inspected regularly a method of fixing which allows easy removal for repairs or relocation is important. In places where boxes are not to be inspected, the method of fixing must allow the tree to grow.

## PRESERVATIVES AND MAINTENANCE

Any wood preservative helps prolong box life. The cheapest is creosote. The golden type dries more quickly, and is easier to apply. Other preservatives can be expensive, Cuprinol and Sadolin PX65 have been recommended but there are several more brands coming onto the market which are claimed to have similar properties. Treat the outside of the box only. The long term effects of preservatives on birds are not known, but can be lethal to bats which may be casual nestbox occupants. Do not risk treating the insides of boxes. Boxes can be camouflaged to some extent by treating with preservatives in two colours - either two shades of creosote or creosote with wood stain added.

Minor repairs can often be done on the spot. A kit consisting of hammer, pincers, nails, string and rubber, formica or metal patches is adequate for many jobs including dealing with holes enlarged by squirrels. Major repairs are best done by putting up new boxes and taking the damaged ones for repair in a workshop. In places where grey squirrel or woodpecker damage is frequent, it will pay to reinforce the entrance with sheet metal before the box is put up or to enclose the box with a jacket of chicken wire.

All boxes should be cleaned annually. Owl, Swift, hirundine and tit nests are generally heavily infested with various parasites and must be cleaned by the autumn. Allow 2 or 3 weeks after fledging before cleaning to ensure not to disrupt a possible second brood. If you delouse boxes use a dry short lived natural based insecticide such as pyrethrum powder. Leave a layer of soft material like wood shavings, bark chippings or even polystyrene packing chips in large boxes. Sawdust is not particularly good for lining the bottom of large boxes, as it will clog the drainage holes and when wet is too hard to be workable by the birds. Renew polystyrene foam in excavatable boxes aimed at woodpeckers or Willow Tits in the winter or early spring. Check all boxes in late winter to make any necessary repairs before the breeding season.

Rafts, islands and artificial banks will need annual overhauls or checks. Early spring is the best time once the worst winter weather is past. Rafts which are not needed for winter roosting may be brought ashore for the winter to avoid undue storm and bird dropping damage.

# LOCATION

The direction that the box faces makes little difference provided that it is sheltered from prevailing wind, rain and strong sunlight. The sector from north through east to south east is possibly the most favourable but in shady woodland other considerations like slope of the trunk will override that of direction. Keep boxes away from the wet side of a tree trunk where the rain water flows down in a torrent (page 16). It is usually possible to see where the rain water runs down the trunk from the growth of green algae, but if in doubt wait for rain! To give additional shelter to the entrance of small boxes, angle them forwards slightly particularly if the nestbox roof has little overhang. Larger open boxes should be mounted tilted slightly upwards so that the nest rests naturally in the rearmost part of the box. If possible locate away from predators (this may be impossible in many cases, weasels for example can climb almost anything, but boxes in gardens can be placed where cats cannot climb). Prickly or thorny bushes make good sites although inspection can sometimes be hazardous. For many species the height of the box is not important (Species Notes give more detailed guidance). It may range from 1m upwards and will depend on ease of inspection, visibility etc. Boxes high on tree trunks are less easy to reach by marauding humans, but may be more visible than lower boxes concealed in the shrub layer of a wood. Except for species which, like Treecreeper, walk into the nestbox the hole entrance must be clear enough from the trunk to allow a convenient flight path in.

The density of boxes depends on the habitat and species involved. A good plan is to begin with a few boxes more or less uniformly spaced, and keep adding until it is clear that lack of nest sites is no longer limiting the population. About ten assorted small boxes to the hectare is a typical density. Colonial species may nest very densely, but in this case try and make all the boxes appear different from each other - a column of identical nestboxes mounted on a telegraph pole would be a recipe for total confusion. Place nestboxes at different height, on different trees and facing in different directions. For non-colonial species, do not put boxes up at such a density that they encourage aggressive behaviour between over close neighbours. For bird population studies, an excess of boxes is desirable although it is generally not possible to have 100% of the population using boxes. For most species 50% of the population using boxes is a high success rate. If you find most of your boxes are occupied successfully you should put up more boxes.

Boxes are often successful in attracting large numbers of birds of many species when placed near the boundaries between habitats, in a mosaic of habitats or in small isolated habitats. Such places include woodland edges or rides, along hedgerows, small copses, along stream sides and in isolated trees.

Garden nestboxes should never be placed adjacent to bird tables or other feeding devices. Large numbers of feeding birds will disturb potential nesting pairs and attract predators. 'Attractive' garden centre type boxes with integral bird table should be avoided.

The best time to put up boxes is as soon as they are available. Birds may use them at any time of the year for roosting if not nesting. Some birds may need to select nesting sites very early (e.g. during early autumn by Tree Sparrows, and mid-winter by Tawny Owls) so even boxes put up in summer will not be wasted. Occasionally boxes are not used for several years after siting. It may be worth resiting smaller boxes after three or four years, larger ones after six or more years.

Nestboxes are obviously most urgently needed in places where natural holes are scarce but where food is plentiful. Such places include managed woodland where mature trees are cropped and dead wood removed, farmland with the tall trees removed from hedges and old buildings cleared, young forestry plantations and many gardens.

With larger boxes for species under threat, such as Barn Owl, make a thorough survey of the area first. Obtain the landowner's permission and encourage his on-site support. Boxes in the vicinity of recently occupied sites may be successful in helping to expand the range of a species locally. Boxes close to a threatened used site (like a dead tree or derelict barn possibly due for removal) may help to keep a species in the area. Large boxes are very visible to humans and so should be sited with great care. It is better not to put up a box, rather than to have a pair of birds whose eggs are stolen year after year. All birds are protected by law, but some rare or threatened species (on a list called Schedule 1) have special provisions. It is illegal to inspect nests of these birds without a government licence. The Appendix gives more information about obtaining licences.

Take care with ladders. The safest and most useful type is a lightweight alloy extendable ladder with splayed feet for stability. Always have a second person to steady any but the shortest of ladders. An extra C-shaped top rung will make the ladder more stable when leaning on small diameter tree trunks.

Any operations involving large numbers of boxes or large and heavy structures require much time and manpower. Many time consuming problems can arise in the field but thorough planning will go some way to avoiding them. Survey the area in winter when lack of leaf cover makes work easier. Time spent in devising efficient methods will be amply rewarded by time and frustration saved in the field. Check-lists of equipment and materials needed are useful. Perhaps simulate the operation with model 'boxes' (e.g. Lego pieces placed on a large map of the site) before embarking on the real thing. It is easier to move wrongly placed models on a map than real ones in the field. Note problems which crop up in order to be prepared for the next year.

# SAFETY

Many activities concerned with nestboxes are potentially hazardous - even the apparently simple act of nailing a tit box to a house wall. It is impossible to list all precautions which should be taken, but the notes below highlight some points.

Be familiar with the safe working practice for any tool which you use, and do not use implements, particularly power tools, for purposes for which they are not intended. Wear protective glasses when using masonry nails (or inspecting owl boxes). Do not use power-saws on reclaimed wood where there is any possibility of striking a nail. Beware of electricity whether it is in an overhead wire under which you are carrying an aluminium ladder or an unprotected wire in the garden shed to which you are nailing a nestbox.

Ensure ladders are secure before you climb them. Be particularly careful of ladders against thin trees or ladders resting on branches projecting from the main trunk of trees. It is possible to go on tree climbing courses should you need to scale high trees. You should not take part in any activity on cliffs without full training and safety gear. If you are working with rafts or islands be careful not to overload boats or of working from a small unstable boat. Wear a life-jacket for deep water work. For any of these activities at least two workers are better than one.

Whenever we are working with birds we always make safety of the birds paramount. However, the long term interests of birds will not be well served by unsafe activities of nestboxers. An injured or dead nestbox enthusiast cannot do much for the birds, and sadly accidents of such gravity have occurred. **The BTO can accept no liability for any accidents that occur to fieldworkers who use the Nestboxes guide as a basis for their work. Please do not risk injury to yourself. No amount of nestboxing or fieldwork is worth an accident.**

# DESIGNS

Each design is accompanied by illustrations. Diagrams for more conventional boxes begin with an exploded drawing of the various components. A cutting list should be made from this. There is also a general view of each box which includes the names of the various lengths. The dimensions required for particular species are given under Species Notes. On any one page of illustrations the scale may vary from one diagram to another. The illustrations serve to give a overall idea of the design and to highlight particular design features.

## HOLE ENTRANCE BOXES

The dimensions given in Species Notes are width, depth from front to back and height respectively. In its most common form, this design is the classic 'Tit Box'. It is basically an enclosed space with a single entrance hole, and with an opening hatch for inspection.

The box must have a watertight roof and side joints but the base construction should allow for drainage. The roof should project over the entrance to provide shelter and shade. A roof which projects over all sides will provide additional protection from rain. Sloping roofs are not essential - boxes are often fixed so that the entrance hole is angled downwards slightly to provide additional shelter and so that rain will drain off such a flat roof. Inspection is normally through the roof on smaller boxes but on larger boxes the upper portion of the front may be a more convenient access.

### Smaller Boxes

For most small birds the only critical factors in construction are entrance diameters which will control the species able to enter. Even so it is probably more a case of excluding unwanted species, rather than attracting the desired ones - birds can use oversize but not undersize holes. An entrance diameter of 28mm will exclude House Sparrows but allow in most other small birds including all the tits and Pied Flycatchers. Some species may tend to select as small a hole as possible. The position of the entrance hole is unimportant as long as it is high on the box. A low hole will let predators like cats or squirrels reach in to take the contents even though the hole will be too small for all the body. Deep boxes also help prevent premature departure by restless or frightened young. The hole may be either at the front or side provided that when the box is in position the hole is sheltered from the elements and is far enough away from obstructions to allow the birds an easy flight path. Some workers prefer to cut a rectangular notch in the rear top corner of the box, rather than bore a round hole, although this practice does make access easier for mammals. As a rough guide, boxes should be large enough in section to allow access to an adult human hand. This will allow cleaning of the box and, if a trained and licensed person is available, ringing of the young. Up to a point, larger boxes will provide conditions for larger broods but excessively large boxes are not advantageous as they require the birds to find a great deal of nesting material. A volume of 10 litres for example is the maximum required for Great Tits and 4 litres for Blue Tits. Very small boxes should be adequately ventilated to prevent overheating of young in case one hungry nestling should spend a long time nearly blocking the entrance hole. This can be achieved by boring some small holes sloping upwards from the outside in the upper part of the sides.

### Large Boxes

Unless very wide and good quality wooden planks are available, these boxes should have an inner framework to strengthen the structure. The hole is most conveniently made as a rectangular cut out at the top of the front. Drainage holes are very important. Various ready

# HOLE ENTRANCE BOXES

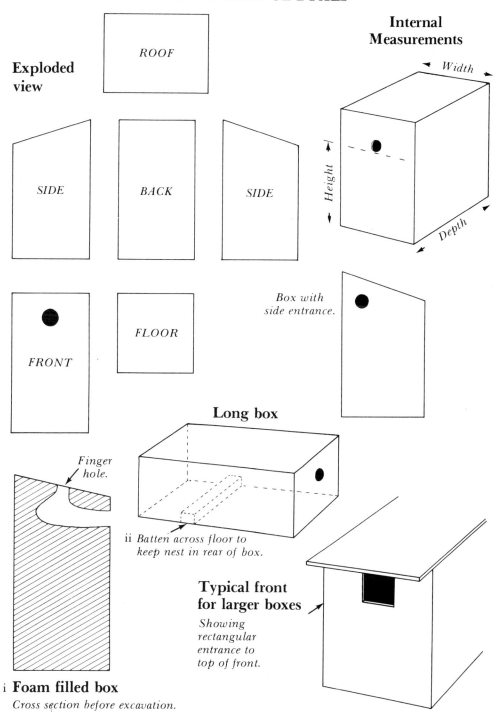

**Exploded view**

ROOF

SIDE

BACK

SIDE

FRONT

FLOOR

**Internal Measurements**

Width

Height

Depth

*Box with side entrance.*

**Long box**

*ii Batten across floor to keep nest in rear of box.*

*Finger hole.*

**Typical front for larger boxes**

*Showing rectangular entrance to top of front.*

i **Foam filled box**

*Cross section before excavation.*

# HOLE ENTRANCE BOXES

## Sawdust/cement box

*hanging from tree showing lid held down by weight of box.*

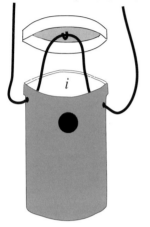

## Barn Owl Box

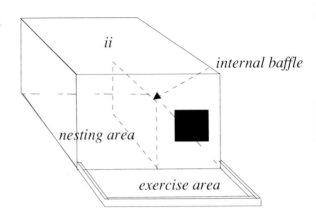

*internal baffle*

*nesting area*

*exercise area*

## Swift box,

*view from below.*

*Inspection hatch above nesting chamber.*

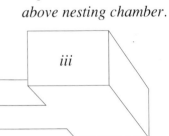

*Entrance*

*Nesting chamber wider and higher than tunnel.*

*Watertight roof.*

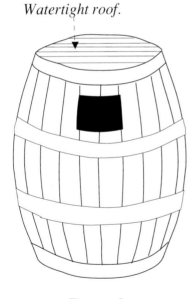

## Barrels,

*alternative positions.*

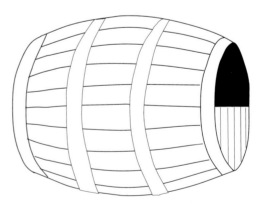

made boxes can be adapted easily. These include barrels with an entrance hole cut out, but do not use plywood tea chests or packing cases except as indoor boxes. Most larger species prefer the nestbox to have a layer of loose dry material over the floor. The best material is chopped dry bark (garden shredder output is ideal) but shavings can be used instead. Peat and other softer materials should not be used because they tend to retain moisture and heat up as they decompose.

## Filled Boxes

For birds like woodpeckers and Willow Tits which excavate nests, boxes should be filled with a soft inert material. Expanded polystyrene is most easily obtainable. More expensive balsa wood may be used. Woodshavings and sawdust have been used for Lesser Spotted Woodpeckers and Willow Tits. Fill the box with several layers of the material rather than one single piece. This will allow easier inspection. Excavate a small gap behind the entrance hole to give the impression of the beginning of a hole, but ensure this cavity is too small for a Wren to nest in. The top layer should have a finger hole cut in to allow easy lifting out for inspection (page 21i). These boxes are best refilled after being used because their users usually excavate a fresh chamber before nesting again.

## Long Boxes

Some birds such as Little Owl or Redstart may prefer a long low cavity to the more conventional deep tit box. With these boxes the length rather than the depth protects the occupants from long armed predators provided the nest is made at the rear of the box. To encourage this incorporate a low dividing ridge across the middle of the floor (page 21ii). The entrance hole should be in the upper part of the front panel. The inspection hatch must give access to the rear of the box. These boxes may be fixed projecting from the trunk or slung under branches to simulate a rotten bough. Redstarts in some areas seem only to take to these boxes.

## Barn Owl Box

Barn Owls need a very large nestbox, but since they will often nest within buildings it need not be of weatherproof material. Old tea chests and packing cases are ideal. The entrance hole should be placed towards the bottom of the front section and preferably should open onto a ledge with a lip around it. The ledge should be about 30cm long and as wide as the nestbox. This will provide a safe exercise area for the young. The inspection hatch may be at any convenient part of the box from which the full contents can be reached. Barn Owl boxes which are to be sited in trees must be very soundly constructed - tea chests will not do.

## Swift Box

This is a long low box with the entrance hole underneath one end. It may be sited inside a loft with the end projecting through the brickwork, or hung underneath the eaves. Boxes sited inside houses may be made of plywood; even the projecting end will not suffer the worst of our weather since the box can be taken inside from September to April. The inspection hatch will be at the opposite end to the entrance. It is preferable to make the nesting chamber at the far end of the box both higher and wider than at the entrance end - making the box resemble a long low passage leading to a larger room (page 22iii).

## House Martin Box

This box resembles as closely as possible the natural domed shape of the House Martin nest and can be made of papier-mâché, pottery, glued paper or sawdust/cement. Inspection is through a hole in a false roof, or by making the box removable. This can be done either by fixing with two wing nuts or by a sliding arrangement using cup hooks. If a natural nest is not available, a ball of diameter about 150mm can be used as a mould to make two boxes. For ease of construction, place the ball on top of a large jar. This will hold it steady while layers of glued paper or papier mâché are applied (page 14).

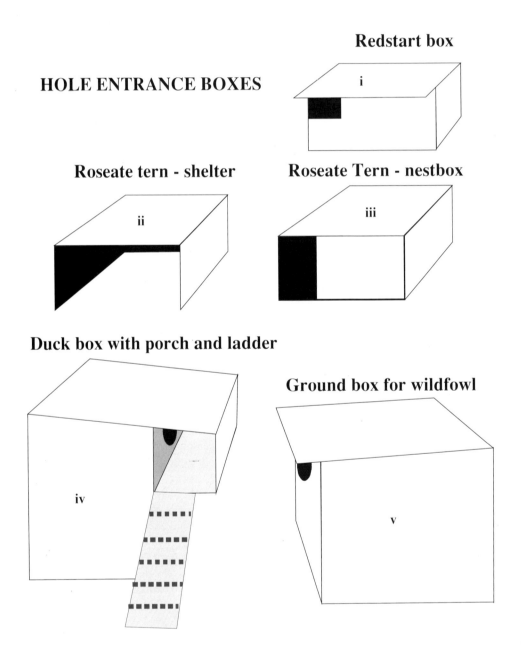

**Redstart box**

i

**HOLE ENTRANCE BOXES**

**Roseate tern - shelter**

ii

**Roseate Tern - nestbox**

iii

**Duck box with porch and ladder**

iv

**Ground box for wildfowl**

v

# OPEN FRONTED BOXES

The dimensions given under Species Notes are width, depth from front to back and height (page 26).

These designs are basically a box in which the upper part of the front is cut away. Since the access hole is so large there is generally no need for the complications of inspection hatches. Boxes with only a very narrow entrance should have an opening roof for inspection. Roofs of other boxes can be nailed or screwed on, but as for hole entrance boxes there should be an overhang to provide shelter. Traditionally, small boxes have been made with the roof sloping down from back to front. Less pleasing to the eye, but possibly a little better in the rain, are roofs sloping to one side. Rain will drain off away from the open front.

Large boxes should have a two or three centimetre diameter branch nailed along the top edge of the front to give a firm perch. Kestrel boxes should have this perch projecting to one side.

Some users have had success with 'open' boxes with about one third of the front fully boarded to the roof. This gives additional privacy to the incubating bird but fully open fronted boxes seem to suit all regular species. Kittiwakes and Spotted Flycatchers, on the other hand, will use boxes that are no more than a ledge.

All open fronted boxes are vulnerable to predators and so should be sited very carefully. Some measures can be taken against predators and these are listed under Pests and Predators. Larger boxes are less easy to protect and may suffer substantial (but not unnaturally heavy) predation. Visibility to predators should be considered when siting these boxes, although some species like Spotted Flycatcher and Pied Wagtail tend to prefer open positions or positions with a clear outlook. If you try such boxes remember they are very prone to predation and are best sited on sheer faces such as house walls or amongst a screen of climbing plants.

# CHIMNEY BOXES

This box was designed specifically for Tawny Owls but has also been used by other species including Kestrel, Stock Dove, Robin, Great Tit, Jackdaw and Starling.

The box has a more or less square cross section, is open at one end and closed at the other. It is generally mounted at an angle of about 45° to horizontal although the angle is not critical. The base, which may be of wood or metal, must have adequate drainage holes since some rain will invariably enter the box. The floor should be covered with bark chippings or similar before use. The upwards facing joints between panels must be waterproof. If in doubt, use roofing felt. The box is very deep so inspection will be through a hatch, preferably in one side. The hatch should be at least 20cm. above the floor to prevent eggs or young falling out. Any method of locking the hatch is acceptable, the wooden turn-buttons illustrated are as convenient as any. The uppermost side can be extended forwards to provide additional shelter against rain. A two or tree centimetre diameter branch fixed across the bottom of the entrance will provide a landing perch. Remote inspection may be through a mirror permanently clamped to an arm fixed at the entrance.

Boxes may be fixed in a number of ways. They may be secured either under (page 27i) or over (page 27ii) an existing branch by wire but remember to loosen each season. They can be fixed using a batten firmly screwed along one side of the box at 45° to the end and screwed to a vertical tree trunk (page 27iii). They may have a long batten screwed across the top end of one side then wedged into a suitable fork in the tree (page 27iv). In this case the batten may not need securing to the tree. Finally they may be fixed at 45° to the trunk of a tree using two wire stays and by nailing the bottom of the box to the trunk (page 27v). This simulates a broken off and hollowed branch.

# OPEN FRONTED BOXES

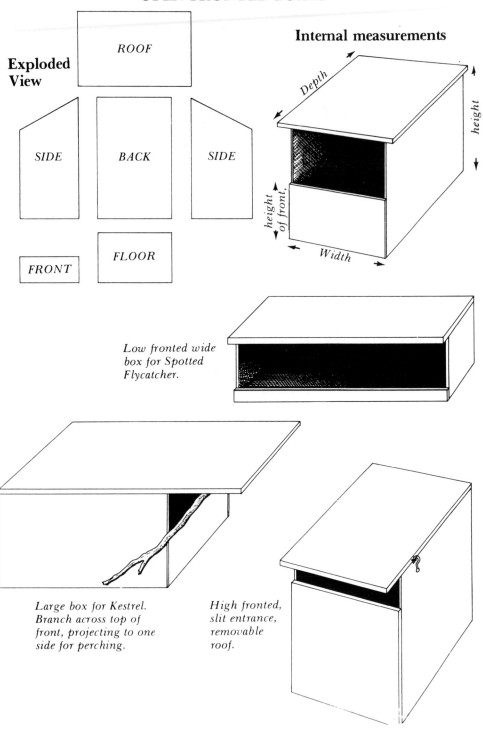

**Exploded View**

ROOF

SIDE  BACK  SIDE

height of front.

FRONT  FLOOR

**Internal measurements**

Depth

height

Width

Low fronted wide box for Spotted Flycatcher.

Large box for Kestrel. Branch across top of front, projecting to one side for perching.

High fronted, slit entrance, removable roof.

# CHIMNEY BOXES

## Internal measurements

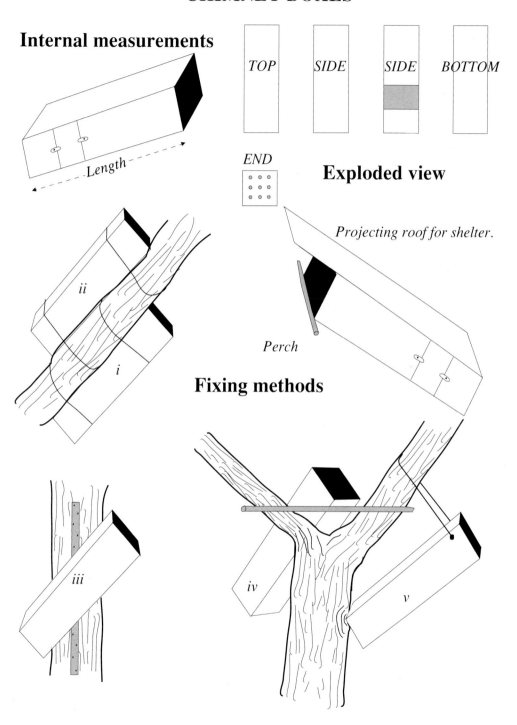

TOP    SIDE    SIDE    BOTTOM

END

## Exploded view

*Projecting roof for shelter.*

*Perch*

## Fixing methods

*Length*

*ii*

*i*

*iii*

*iv*

*v*

# TUNNELS

## Tunnel

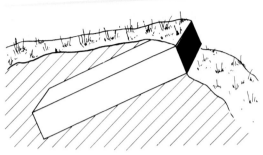

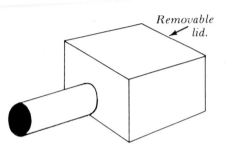

## Tunnel and chamber

### Tunnel with inspection entrance

Outer lid. Inspection shaft.

Inner inspection cover.

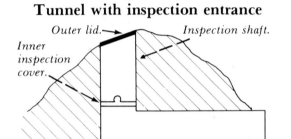

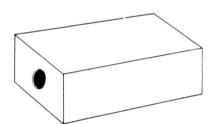

*Tunnel — a long floorless hole entrance box sited on ground.*

*Artificial bank for Sand Martin.*

*Overhanging top with vegetation.*

*Face rendered with cement except over tunnel entrance.*

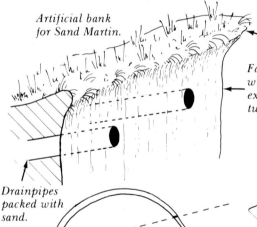

*Drainpipes packed with sand.*

*40 gal. drum with partial soil filling. Note nesting chamber at end.*

*Kingfisher nest chamber of fibreglass. Chambers are made in 2 sections and held together by wire. Note drainage holes.*

# TUNNELS

Tunnels are boxes sited on or under ground, with or without a larger nesting chamber at one end. They may be used by a wide variety of birds including Storm Petrel, Puffin, Shelduck, Kingfisher, and Wheatear, The dimensions given are the cross-section and length of the tunnel, and floor area and height of the chamber.

Wood can be used for construction, but often other materials are more convenient or better. These include bricks and flat stones, drainage pipes, driftwood and turf. Tunnels should in most cases be covered with local materials, e.g. a stone cairn on a shingle beach, or built into a natural or artificial bank. They should slope upwards gently from the entrance to allow for drainage, particularly if the floor is waterproof.

Tunnels can be made of concrete or fibreglass sections formed in a suitably shaped mould. The advantage of these over ready-made clay pipes is that the cross section can be made exactly as required rather than circular only.

Some species, such as Kingfisher and Sand Martin, excavate holes. For them, tunnels should be made and softly packed with local materials leaving only a very short section unfilled at the entrance.

Inspection, where feasible, may be through a hatch in the far end of the tunnel or in the nesting chamber. Access to the hatch will be through the covering material. Clean non-inspectable tunnels annually with a long hook.

Tunnels need not have integral floors, though small tunnels are safer with them. Tunnels should have a layer of local material like shingle over the floor.

Many species using tunnels may undertake excavation themselves beyond the limits of the artificial tunnel provided. It is, therefore important that the nesting chamber roof does not collapse if such excavation takes place. Even for smaller species such as Kingfisher and Sand Martin a 60cm square paving slab, supported firmly around its edges should be used. Pack the hole below with natural material leaving just a normal sized nest chamber to start with. If you need to inspect the nest, the paving slab will need a central access hole.

The entrance to tunnels is usually of the same cross-section as the rest of the tunnel, but a few species such as Wheatear require smaller entrances. This may be arranged either by providing the tunnel an end with a hole bored in it, or more easily by partially blocking the entrance with stone. The shape of the cross-section of the tunnel is often not important. Round pipes will do as well as square wooden tunnels.

Predators can be a particular problem with boxes at ground level. The only precautions (other than those mentioned in Pests and Predators) that can be taken are to peg down smaller boxes firmly and to incorporate a mat of barbed wire in the outer burden above the nest chamber. This will secure them against uprooting by foxes or dogs. There have been some reports of predators breaking into floorless tunnels from below. If this is a problem, embed wire mesh in the soil a little under the tunnel.

# RAFTS

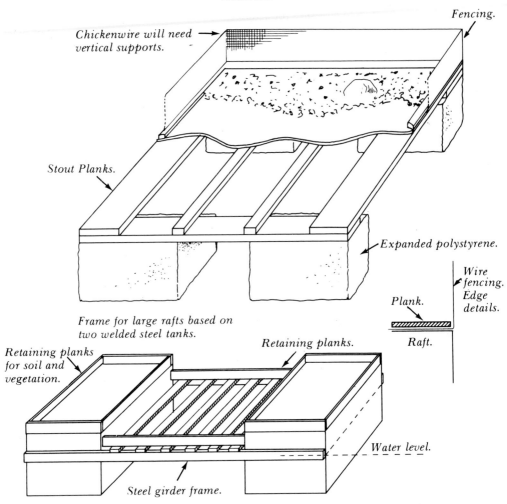

Fencing.

Chickenwire will need vertical supports.

Stout Planks.

Expanded polystyrene.

Wire fencing. Edge details.

Plank.

Raft.

Frame for large rafts based on two welded steel tanks.

Retaining planks for soil and vegetation.

Retaining planks.

Water level.

Steel girder frame.

## Small raft with vegetation

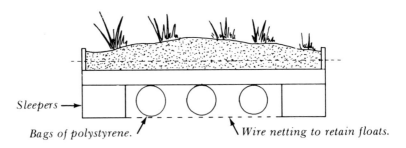

Sleepers

Bags of polystyrene.

Wire netting to retain floats.

# RAFTS

Rafts and islands provide nest sites for a variety of species including various divers, grebes, ducks, geese and swans. They are relatively safe from predators and are useful on waters where the banks are over-disturbed by fishing etc, but the rest of the water is undisturbed, or where the banks are of inhospitable concrete. In addition to the target species many casuals have nested in the vegetation growing on rafts. These include, for example, Moorhen, Sedge Warbler and Reed Bunting. Gravel extraction companies may be persuaded to provide materials and labour for rafts which are to be sited on flooded gravel pits; local councils or naturalists trusts may do the same for rafts on reservoirs. The same spectrum of species use rafts as use islands. Islands are harder to construct but do last very much longer than rafts. Rafts are most useful in deep water or water whose level varies, otherwise islands may be preferable. Raft designs vary widely depending on materials and skills available as well as the target species. The RSPB River and Wildlife Handbook gives many more ideas and details.

The basic sequence in raft construction is:

     1  Construct frame.
     2  Add platform, floats and fittings
     3  Add soil/gravel/ballast until the raft floats at the correct level
     4  Anchor on station

## Frame

Four railway sleepers or telegraph poles bolted together in a square with less substantial timbers laid across this frame to provide support for the decking will make a serviceable base. Smaller rafts will need correspondingly smaller timbers. If angle girders, welding equipment and skills are available, use them.

## Platform

This will depend on the type of raft. For rafts to hold vegetation some wire mesh or gridweld provides the best base. This will allow water access to the roots of the plants but will need a strong supporting frame below. For rafts without vegetation, use a wooden platform. Marine ply is the best material, but any sheets of wood will do. Even old doors will last a season or two. Ensure that there are no small gaps between boards through which young birds might fall.

## Floats

Welded steel tanks make the best floats, but these are not easily available and will require professional skills to incorporate them into the raft structure. With large rectangular tanks the top surface can be used as the platform. In this case it will need a high lip added to retain soil, and arrangements may be made for watering the soil. Once plants are established, rain water will probably be adequate. A raft consisting of a single large tank will be over-buoyant and may be unstable unless adequately weighted below.

Other floats are cheaply available from scrap heaps and building sites. These include:

Polystyrene blocks. These may deteriorate in very rough conditions but are otherwise long lasting and easy to attach. They are held underneath the raft by gravity and a few long pegs through the frame and block to stop sideways movement. Some smaller rafts have used floats of bits of polystyrene enclosed in netting, or enclosed between the platform and netting stretched underneath the frame.

200 litre drums. Metal drums rust quickly and need replacing frequently but are fairly easy to obtain. Plastic drums may become brittle in winter but are valuable in the short term. If you rely on hollow air filled floats of any sort, ensure you have some insurance against puncturing.

# Construction of mattress raft

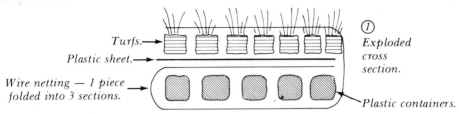

Turfs.→

Plastic sheet.→

Wire netting — 1 piece folded into 3 sections. →

① Exploded cross section.

Plastic containers.

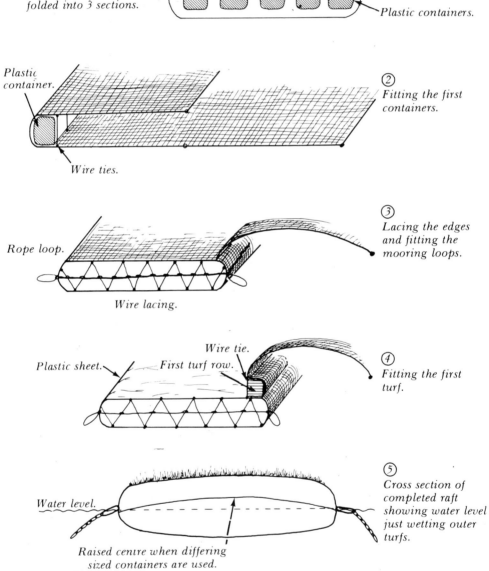

Plastic container.

Wire ties.

② Fitting the first containers.

Rope loop.

Wire lacing.

③ Lacing the edges and fitting the mooring loops.

Wire tie.

Plastic sheet.

First turf row.

④ Fitting the first turf.

Water level.

⑤ Cross section of completed raft showing water level just wetting outer turfs.

Raised centre when differing sized containers are used.

Floats can be filled with polystyrene before sealing, for example. Using many small containers rather than one or two large ones as floats reduces the risk of sudden catastrophic failure because of puncturing.

## Fittings

All rafts need arrangements for mooring. These can be two steel rings fixed to opposite corners of the raft.

Rafts with vegetation (for divers, grebes, wildfowl and rails) need retaining walls. Logs or planks will do, but there must be easy access from the water to the raft. If the raft eventually floats with much freeboard then there should be access ramps sloping down to water level. For the species above it is vital that the retaining wall is low enough for chicks to clamber over and reach water in case they need to leave the raft quickly.

Rafts with no vegetation (for terns or Little Ringed Plover) must have a retaining fence about 25cm high around the raft to prevent young from falling overboard. The fence should be of wire mesh with adequate vertical supports. The top of the fence should be finished safely since adult terns will use it for perching on. The fence is vital if tern nests are to be inspected or the young ringed - young terns will abandon ship on the arrival of 'inspectors' if there is no perimeter fence. If shingle is to be placed on the decking, place a black polythene sheet on the raft first. This will help prevent growth of vegetation. There should be a low lip around the raft perimeter (a plank laid flat will do) to retain shingle. A number of larger stones should be sited on the deck to assist the birds and nest recorders to map the nests. Alternatively, a number of wooden tomato trays can be filled with shingle and placed on the deck. Rafts should incorporate shelter from wind and rain for young birds. A few upturned wooden boxes with one side knocked out can be fastened to the decking for this purpose - the shelters illustrated for Roseate Terns (page 24) are quite adequate. Alternatively small branches will suffice but do not use boxes which are big enough for wildfowl to nest in.

## Ballast

Soil or gravel should be added once the decking is secure. Use these materials to weight the raft until it floats correctly. Ensure it is not top heavy. If it is, reduce top weight and add scrap iron under the frame. The depth of soil must be sufficient to allow moisture retention and plant growth. Ideally the soil should touch the water allowing constant irrigation. Plant the raft with useful species such as hard rush (*Juncus inflexus*). Other local plants should also be used. Very large rafts may take small shrubs. Nestboxes for wildfowl can be sited on rafts.

## The Mattress Raft

This design has been used successfully in Scotland and elsewhere for divers and other waterbirds. The raft consists of a layer of plastic drums of capacities 5 litres to 25 litres as available. These support a 30cm deep layer of turf. The layers are held together with plastic coated fence wire netting tied with plastic coated wire of a similar gauge. Between the turf and floats is a layer of tough polythene (e.g. Visqueen 500g) which retains soil until the turf roots bind it together. The mattress floats with the bottom of the soil just touching the water. Since this raft without turf is light it can be constructed away from the waterside then taken to the launching place before turf is added. Rope loops at the corners make carrying handles and are used for mooring. The turfs must not be placed on the raft until it is floating. As more turf is loaded on, float the raft in deeper water. Dragging a 2 tonne raft across a beach is damaging to raft and humans alike!

The numbered illustrations show the stages in construction. (1) An exploded cross section of the raft. For a 3m x 2m raft you need a 9m x 2m length of netting folded into three equal lengths. (2) Tie each container to both lower and middle wire layers pulling wire ties tightly. If the containers are of varying sizes, place largest ones in the centre. (3) Lace the edges of the raft together tightly with wire and thread with a rotproof rope around the perimeter of the raft leaving 30cm diameter loops at each corner. Lay the plastic sheet over the container layer and tie it in place. (4) Place turfs on the top, row by row, starting at the end with the fold in the wire. As each turf is laid, tie it in tightly with wire to the upper and central netting layers. The plastic sheet will need to be punctured to achieve this. Lace the upper edges together in the same manner as for the lower edges.

## Mooring

Anchor the raft using two weights and chains. Weights can be made of rubble and concrete in strong containers or of scrap iron. Substantial anchors have been made by wrapping several boulders in a length of plastic covered fence wire netting in a manner similar to the mattress raft construction. Anchors of about 300kg are adequate for most situations. For stability the mooring lines should slope up to the raft rather than being vertical. The two anchor lines should also be attached to opposite corners of the raft so that the plan view shows the anchors and raft in a straight line along the direction of the prevailing wind. Anchors can be conveniently carried to their dropping point using the raft as a barge. Tow the raft using a boat, or on smaller waters using hauling teams pulling from both near and far shores. Remember to tie a long enough rope with buoy to the anchor before you drop it! The rafts should be moored far from the shore and disturbance, but preferably in sheltered situations such as inlets or bays.

If the water level fluctuates the raft will hold its position better with long mooring lines at a shallow angle rather than steep, shorter mooring lines. Ensure that the mooring lines can cope with the maximum depth which is likely to be encountered. If the fluctuations through the year are very great it may be necessary to have a means of adjusting the lengths of the mooring lines.

When anchoring rafts take particular care to ensure that you and your crew are well clear of the anchor rope as the anchor is dropped.

## Maintenance

Rafts should be checked once or twice annually and any damage to structure or plants made good. If rafts are not needed by birds over winter they should be brought ashore. This saves wear and tear from weather and loafing gulls. Remember to fix a marker float to the mooring lines when bringing in a raft. Plastic containers make good buoys, but even on small waters they can be very difficult to spot - mark them with bright colours or attach a bamboo pole and flag.

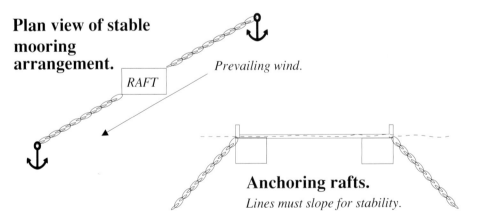

**Plan view of stable mooring arrangement.**

*Prevailing wind.*

RAFT

**Anchoring rafts.**

*Lines must slope for stability.*

# PLATFORMS

Platforms are structures on which nests are to be built. For small birds, almost any old box, tray or even coconut shell fastened in an appropriate site will do. Ensure any such platform has adequate shelter, drainage and concealment. Simple platforms can also be made from weldmesh bent into a bowl shape.

Large platforms, particularly for raptors will need a strong frame. A triangle or an inverted triangular pyramid are the best shapes for strong frames. The frame supports a cup of weldmesh with a 'nest' built into it. The nest should be made of pliable twigs woven into the weldmesh, This ensures firm attachment of the nest to the frame. Smaller twigs are woven into the first ones. Cap the twigs with a layer of peat or inverted turf and make a depression in the centre of this. Secure the frame in place with wire.

Wicker baskets and even sturdy seed trays have been used as platforms in various places. An old Crow or Magpie nest can be used for lining the platform or tray. Old displaced corvid nests have been used on their own, tied securely into tree forks. This operation is useful in an emergency when an occupied nest with young has fallen.

Platforms have been made for wildfowl using a weldmesh cup filled with waterweeds and attached to the top of a short pole. The platform should be sited just above the highest annual water level, in a secluded place.

A platform for Swallows can be made from papier-mâché or sawdust/cement in the shape of a Swallow nest using the same techniques as for the House Martin nest. A second type of platform for Swallows is illustrated below and consists of four flat pieces of wood providing a top, base, back and partition.

Some nature reserves have successfully used 'oil rig' platforms for nests of Little Terns. These are fish boxes filled with shingle and raised on three wooden posts hammered into the beach (read Species Notes for more information).

## PLATFORMS

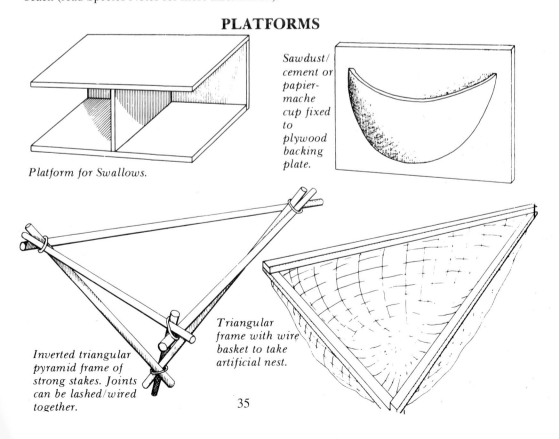

Platform for Swallows.

Sawdust/cement or papier-mache cup fixed to plywood backing plate.

Inverted triangular pyramid frame of strong stakes. Joints can be lashed/wired together.

Triangular frame with wire basket to take artificial nest.

# ISLANDS

Artificial islands are most useful in relatively shallow waters which maintain a stable level. Even in relatively small ponds a suitable island can be made from a 200 litre drum with one end removed. Fill the drum with rubble and soil, stand it on end in the pond with the top just above water level and plant it with rushes or sedges which will provide cover for a nesting Moorhen. Ensure the sides of the drum are punctured to allow water to flow in and out. If space allows, a larger island can be made using several drums or concrete manhole pipes standing together and filled in the same way.

Some natural islands with traditional nesting sites for geese or swans are prone to flooding. These sites can be made safe by raising their level. Do this by laying one or more old lorry tyres on the site and fill them with stones, soil and turf. Brace the structure with stakes if there is more than one tyre in the pile.

Larger islands, like rafts, fall into two main groups - those with and those without vegetation. Those without do not need a gently sloping access from the water and are easier to construct. Form a retaining wall of large blocks or thick wooden stakes. The wall must not have potential nesting sites for Coot which may disturb nesting terns. Fill the enclosure with rubble then successively finer layers of pebbles, capping it with gravel. Take steps to prevent plant growth - a layer of black plastic sheeting below the top gravel layer for example. The gravel layer will need annual raking over to keep it growth free, and can be pock marked with stones as for a tern raft. An alternative to this island is to make a deck exactly as for a tern raft. This deck is secured to posts or scaffold poles driven into the bed of the water. As with rafts the decking needs regular checking.

Most islands have been built in inland freshwater sites, but marine inlets, sea lochs and bays may provide suitable sites. Islands in tidal areas will need protection from wave action. Breakwaters can be made from wooden stakes. Outer rows of stakes may break up waves and inner rows can encourage accretion of shingle. Islands of this type may not be practical in exposed situations. Further, the protective stakes interrupt the smooth slope of the shingle and make the site unattractive to Little Terns.

For islands with vegetation proceed as above but steps must be taken to ensure several easy access points for birds from the water. Each access point must slope gently to the water and must be long enough to allow for any changes in water level. Many water birds like a secluded access to the island so avoid a barren concrete slipway. If erosion is a problem an offshore breakwater can be made from wooden stakes or concrete blocks. Finish the top of the island with soil and turf. Plant the top, sides and shoreline with local plants. Shrubs and small trees will help in stabilising the structure. Place appropriate nesting boxes on the island. It is probably not worthwhile constructing islands without a retaining wall except in very sheltered waters - islands may be completely eroded before the vegetation around the edges stabilises the structure. The only satisfactory 'all natural' islands are those made by cutting off a spit of land which projects into the water. Such spits are often found in gravel pits. In such a case the gravel company may be persuaded to do the excavation during the normal course of gravel extraction operations. Take extra steps here to ensure that the sides of the island are not too steep and ensure adequate vegetation is planted around the edges. These islands have the advantages of a stable structure, but may suffer from proximity to the shore. The ideal shape for very large islands is cross shaped, providing four bays which will give shelter from adverse weather from any quarter. The shape will also allow a higher density of nesting rails and wildfowl.

# NEST BUNDLES

Faggots of sticks can be employed for nest sites and are ideal for use in gardens. Any sticks will do but thorny ones, though more painful to work with, will provide a better result. Make a faggot up to 2m in length and tied at both ends. Open a cavity in the middle and secure it in an open position using some arrangement of wire or wood. Fix the faggot vertically against a tree trunk or in any other site. A climbing plant like honeysuckle or clematis grown over the bundle will help to camouflage the nest. Another nest site can be made by fashioning a cup shaped depression in the top of the faggot. In this case ensure the outer sticks are strong and firmly tied.

Variations on the faggot theme include narrow V shaped bundles tied to tree trunks with the nest site in the recess of the V. Bundles of conifer branches will provide relatively well hidden nesting sites for thrushes early in the season before deciduous plants have developed thick cover. Once a bundle has been fixed to a tree trunk, it can be manipulated into shape to allow both concealment from predators and adequate access for the birds.

For some wildfowl a cone-shaped bundle with a hollow centre can be made and placed point upwards on the ground. This type of shelter should be surrounded by concealing vegetation.

## BUNDLES

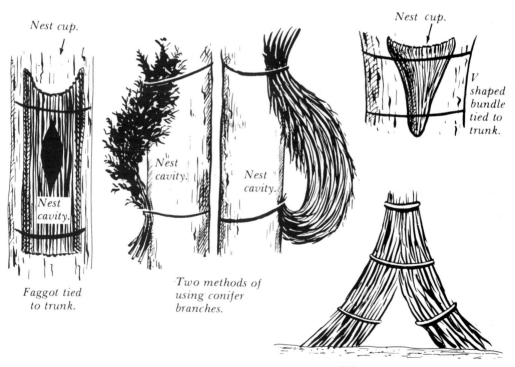

Nest cup.

Nest cavity.

Faggot tied to trunk.

Nest cavity.

Nest cavity.

Two methods of using conifer branches.

Nest cup.

V shaped bundle tied to trunk.

Wigwam for wildfowl.

# TREE AND SHRUB IMPROVEMENT

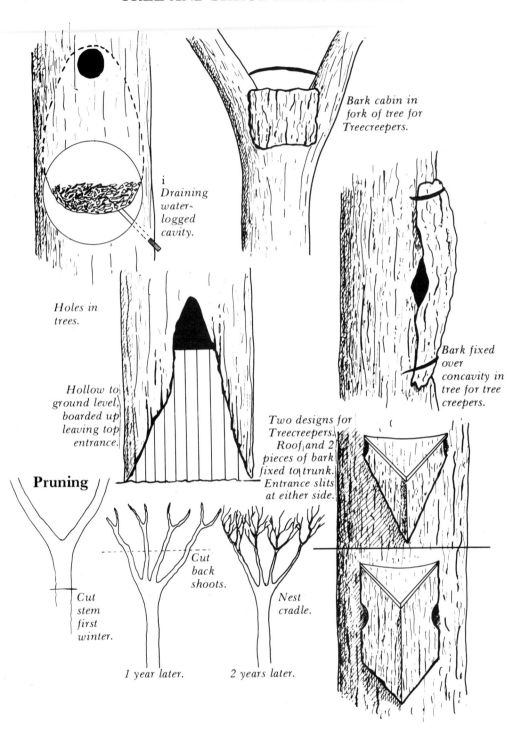

Bark cabin in fork of tree for Treecreepers.

i Draining water-logged cavity.

Holes in trees.

Hollow to ground level, boarded up leaving top entrance.

Bark fixed over concavity in tree for tree creepers.

Two designs for Treecreepers. Roof and 2 pieces of bark fixed to trunk. Entrance slits at either side.

**Pruning**

Cut stem first winter.

Cut back shoots.

Nest cradle.

1 year later.

2 years later.

# TREE AND SHRUB IMPROVEMENT

There are many natural sites which, with some attention, will make attractive nest sites. **Before** carrying out **any** of these operations, including using climbing irons, **ensure you have the landowner's explicit permission**. A general agreement to put up nestboxes is not the same as permission to cut and manipulate trees and shrubs. Some operations will involve heavy and skilled work high in trees. Unless experienced power tool operators are available, hand tools only should be used. In any case, never attempt this type of work alone. Aluminium extension ladders are the most convenient devices for climbing trees quickly, but on the feet of an expert climbing irons have advantages.

Natural holes have the advantage over boxes in that they are less conspicuous to humans. Their main disadvantage (in fact one of the main reasons for nestboxes) is that they are not present in sufficient numbers. The types of operation needed on tree holes are outlined below. They often involve use of metal nails or bars. This is unlikely to affect any commercial value of the tree but it will affect possible future operations with chain saws.

## Waterlogged Hole

Bore a hole through the trunk, upwards towards the lowest part of the cavity. If the floor is not flat, more than one hole may be needed. Once the hole is drained (sludge will need clearing out), insert plastic piping through the holes. The piping should project clear of the trunk. This pipe prevents the hole from becoming sealed as the tree grows. Continued drainage is obviously essential to prevent the hole refilling. Line the cavity base with pebbles, then with shavings or bark chippings. These layers will keep any nest clear of water which runs into the hole. Before draining a cavity ensure that it is not a drinking place for wildlife (page 38i) - a water-filled hole might be a more valuable resource than a nesting site.

## Tree with a large hollow centre

Such holes may be too large for birds to take to readily. Sometimes Barn or Tawny Owls will use these very large holes, so before modifying the hole check for accumulations of pellets. Reduce the depth of the hole by making a false floor. Drill holes around one side of the trunk. Drive pointed metal stakes through these holes across the hollow and firmly in to the other side of the trunk. Saw the ends off flush with the trunk. Cover the grill of bars with large then smaller sticks, finally completing the job with a layer of bark chippings or shavings. Ensure the cavity is not prone to waterlogging.

## Cracks in the side of a cavity

These can be sealed by nailing wood over them. A more lightproof arrangement is to staple layers of sacking over the crack, coating each layer with bituminous paint.

## Entrance hole too small

Use a wood auger to enlarge the hole. This operation may need to be repeated every two or three years.

## Tree with a large hollow open down to ground level

As for apparently over-large holes, check that the cavity is not currently being used (by mammals or birds) before you modify it. The hole can be boarded up nearly to the top. The gap remaining at the top will make the entrance. Use old weathered boards rather than conspicuous painted wood. This type of hole modification is very obvious and should only be attempted in areas fairly safe from human interference.

## Pruning

Various shrubs can be made more useful to nesting birds by judicious pruning. Ensure that any such artificially prepared and attractive sites do not give easy access to predators. Cutting the main stem of the shrub will force a cradle of shoots to grow. This cradle must be pruned again a year later forcing enough shoots to provide a secure concealed nesting site for Blackbirds, thrushes, Goldfinches or Chaffinches.

A circle of young willow saplings can be pulled together and tied about 1m above the ground. This forms a wigwam for a duck or Moorhen to nest under. Clear the floor of the wigwam of woody growth and ensure there is an opening for entry. Similar wigwams may be made using brambles - these could be used by wildfowl or gamebirds.

## Other operations

Holes in soft-wooded trees are frequently depredated by squirrels but can be reinforced as for small nestbox holes. Use a metal plate with a circular cut out, or staple chicken wire around the nest hole area.

Cavities can be started in soft-wooded trees and left to enlarge naturally. Scoop out a cavity where a branch has fallen away or where the tree has been pollarded or coppiced much earlier. This cavity will gradually become bigger, providing potential nest sites for a succession of birds.

Suitable sites for Treecreepers can be made by securing a strip of bark over a concave part of a tree trunk - over an old wound for instance. Entry to the cavity formed must be through both sides of the bark. Alternatively a little bark 'cabin' can be made from three pieces of bark in the fork of a tree. The cabin roof piece should be about 20mm above the top of the walls to give access, and the interior about 50mm deep.

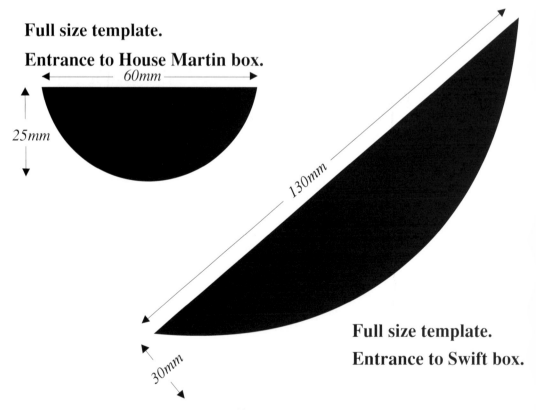

**Full size template.**

**Entrance to House Martin box.**

◄———— 60mm ————►

25mm

130mm

30mm

**Full size template.**

**Entrance to Swift box.**

# SPECIES NOTES

Species are listed below in the systematic Voous order. (This is the order found in most bird identification books.) In addition there are notes for three groups of species - 'tunnel nesting seabirds', 'ground nesting songbirds' and 'open nesting songbirds'. Though species in these groups are not the most regular users of artificial sites and are not closely related, they have very similar nest site requirements. The first group, which includes Manx Shearwater, Storm Petrel and Puffin is placed after grebes, the second which includes Skylark and Yellow Wagtail is placed after woodpeckers and the last, which includes some thrushes, warblers and finches, is placed after Wren. There is an alphabetical species index, which includes scientific names, in the Appendix.

The list excludes a few species which have been very rarely or only locally recorded in artificial nest sites. Jays are excluded because the one nest found in a box is regarded as exceptional. Reed Buntings have been recorded nesting on vegetated rafts and whilst other small ground nesting birds might do the same, it is unlikely that rafts will be constructed exclusively for them. Most species rarely have individuals which will nest in atypical sites but single records of box use must be regarded cautiously. Hoopoe and Wood Duck are not included for their present scarce status does not warrant it. Species which are specially protected under the Wildlife and Countryside Act (1981), and which must not be disturbed at the nest without a licence, have 'Schedule 1' written against their name. Scientific names of birds described in this section are given after the English names.

Each description begins by naming the most suitable artificial nest site design and size. For most boxes the sizes are given as small, medium or large. The table on page 7 under General Instructions gives the approximate dimensions for these categories and also broad height mounting categories.

Boxes which do not fit any of these categories have their approximate dimensions indicated. The height of a hole entrance box is the distance from the hole to the floor. All dimensions are in millimetres except where otherwise indicated. A few sizes are critical, these are noted.

These notes do not give habitat details but these may be found in various other guides (see appendix). Brief details are included of nest structure and eggs. These can only be very general because nest materials vary with local availability and clutch size depends on many factors including weather, time of year, age of bird and habitat. In a typical year you may expect about one quarter of the clutches laid to be outside the quoted ranges.

| | | |
|---|---|---|
| **Divers** | *Gaviidae* | **Schedule 1** |
| Rafts or Islands | Covered with turf and other local vegetation. At least 2m square with freeboard of about 200mm. | |

Divers are fairly conservative in their choice of nesting site and so rafts should be sited where divers have bred successfully in the past or have been seen during the breeding season. It is pointless, however, to site rafts or islands where divers currently breed successfully. Suitable sites include lochs with fluctuating water level or disturbed banks. The raft should be set in a sheltered bay or inlet in water 2-4m deep. This water will be too deep for wading fishermen who might otherwise inadvertently disturb the nest.

Nest: a shallow scrape with variable amounts of vegetation added. Eggs: 2, olive-brown with blackish blotches. Young leave the nest when all the clutch is hatched.

**Great Crested Grebe**      *Podiceps cristatus*
Rafts or Islands      At least 1m square.

The main requirement is a structure on which to anchor the nest. Any raft with a gently sloping access or only 50mm freeboard will do but some cover on the raft is preferable. An island of loosely woven willow twigs, about 1m in diameter and firmly anchored, will make a suitable site. One nest has been recorded built in a floating tyre anchored in a river.

Nest: a heap of vegetation with a slight hollow in centre. Eggs: 3-5, whitish, becoming stained with age. Eggs often covered by nest material. Young leave the nest when all the clutch is hatched.

**Tunnel Nesting Seabirds**
Tunnels

Opportunities for artificial nest sites for these species are clearly limited to a few sites, but at these sites there is potential for many nests. Dimensions of tunnels are not critical - rabbit burrows, which vary in length and cross section, are often used. Tunnels made of flat stones sometimes suffice and there have been tunnels built into harbour walls or the basements of suitably sited houses. All tunnel nesting birds are prone to predation particularly by rats. Manx Shearwater and Storm Petrel are liable to desert if disturbed. Puffin are more tolerant.

**Wildfowl**

Wildfowl may nest fairly densely if there are enough sites so ensure that the habitat can support a potentially large nestbox population of young. Ducklings need warm, shallow and sheltered water with plenty of cover. Many species of duck may take artificial rafts and islands. Mallard are the most regular users. Boxes can be sited on short poles in ponds and shallow lakes. All such wildfowl boxes should have a 50mm roof overhang for shelter and a ladder up to the entrance from water level rising at 45°. The ladder is a plank about 100mm in width with rungs nailed on at about 100mm intervals.

**Swans and Geese**
Rafts, Islands or Platforms in water

The nest site should have adequate sheltering plant growth. If access to the site is steep or overgrown, make a sloping ramp. Mute Swans and Canada Geese are the most frequent users of artificial nest sites.

Nests: Mute Swan nests comprise unmistakably large heaps of vegetation, usually with the cob on guard nearby. Goose nests are typically a shallow hollow in the ground lined with local materials, down and feathers. Eggs: Mute Swan 6, large and off-white. Young remain in the nest for a day or two after hatching. Geese 4-6 eggs, creamy. Young leave the nest soon after hatching.

**Shelduck**      *Tadorna tadorna*
Tunnel and Chamber      Tunnel 200mm diameter, length at least 300mm.
     Chamber 350mm cube.

The tunnel should be sited in a predator free area. An island is ideal. Two simply made tunnel designs are, first, a trench dug in the soil and covered with planks then turf and, second, a 200 litre barrel with the chamber made by partially covering the floor with soil (page 28). Shelducks may also occupy wigwam shaped bundles placed in thick undergrowth. In some areas tunnels made of bales of straw on the ground or in scrub have been used. Shelduck will also take large hole entrance boxes set on the ground (page 24v).

Nest: a hollow lined with local vegetation, down and feathers. Eggs: 8-10, creamy. Young leave nest soon after hatching.

**Mandarin**  *Aix galericulata*
Hole Entrance  Large. Some have used long boxes 700mm deep, 250mm wide and 200mm high with the entrance at one end. Hole entrance 100mm diameter.

 Mandarin seem initially reluctant to take to boxes put up specifically for them. However once the local population have started using boxes they keep to them. Boxes should be placed about 4 m above ground initially, but once the birds have begun to use them the boxes can gradually be sited lower in following seasons. Boxes should be lined with shavings which will remain loose enough for the bird to hide eggs. Large wood shavings may deter Jackdaws which sometimes take over boxes sited for Mandarin.

Nest: lined with vegetable fibres and down. Eggs: 9-12, pale buff and white. Young leave nest within a day of hatching.

**Mallard**  *Anas platyrhynchos*
Rafts, Islands, Platforms
Hole Entrance  About 300mm x 300mm x 220mm high, entrance hole about 150mm diameter

 Mallard will take a wide assortment of sites. Some take to cup-shaped hollows, preferably primed with vegetation. Rafts or islands should have plenty of vegetation and could even have a nestbox mounted on them. A favoured location for a nest is near the mouth of a creek opening onto the main body of water. Mallard are often recorded in bizarre sites including high window boxes. Pollarded willows are often used.

 Mallard like to be able to see out from the nest whilst incubating, so narrow horizontal slits in the sides will help. Traditional wicker duck baskets, mounted tilted slightly backwards on tripods of stakes, minimize predation by rats.

Nest: lined with down and breast feathers. Eggs: 10-12, pale greenish, may be hidden under lining. Young leave nest soon after hatching. Feral birds may rear two broods per year.

**Goldeneye**  *Bucephala clangula*  **Schedule 1**
Hole Entrance, with or without porch  Large/Very Large or larger. Entrance about 115mm diameter.

 The box must be very soundly made and thoroughly waterproofed. The inside should be of rough wood to allow the ducklings to get a claw hold. The birds like a dark interior to the box which is achieved by the internal height of the box. The box should be fixed with a clear view of open water, not more than 10 metres from the water's edge. Initially place boxes in well spaced groups of 3 or 4 boxes in secluded areas. Boxes should be placed in the upper part of the medium height range. Do not worry about high boxes as ducklings can descend from great heights quite safely. Boxes with porches (page 24iv) are used in Scandinavia and on various wildfowl reserves.

Nest: lined with wood chips, down and breast feathers. Eggs: 6-11, blue-green. Young leave the nest soon after hatching.

**Red-breasted Merganser**  *Mergus serrator*
Hole Entrance/Tunnel
 The box should be a long floorless hole entrance box placed on the ground - almost qualifying as a tunnel. Height at least 200mm, width 350mm, depth 450mm. The hole at one end only should be about 120mm in diameter. The box should be placed in thick vegetation facing the water. Take precautions against ground predators.

Nest: lined with plant material, abundant down and some feathers. Eggs: 7-12, stone-buff.

**Goosander**                    *Mergus merganser*
Hole Entrance                    Very Large. Entrance diameter at least 100mm,
                                 preferably up to 160mm high and 150mm wide.

Boxes should be placed at medium height initially up to 30 metres from the water's edge with a clear view of, and flight line to, the water. The edge of a wood adjacent to water is a good site to start with, but later boxes may be moved deeper into the wood. Clumping boxes as for Goldeneye may help initially. *Boxes must only be sited in safe areas because Goosanders are conspicuous and subject to persecution.* Put a layer of dried moss or shavings in the box.

Nest: lined with pieces of rotten wood and much down. Eggs: 8-11, creamy white. Young remain in the nest for one or two days after hatching.

**Birds of Prey**                                          Many **Schedule 1**

Most raptors require an open platform but there has been limited success in providing artificial platforms in this country. Many raptors use old crow or pigeon nests. Osprey platforms (diameter about 2m) have been used in the USA but at present it is probably not worth attempting to attract Ospreys to artificial sites - persecution rather than lack of sites being a limiting factor. There has been recent success with platforms for Goshawk and Red Kite might possibly use them. In cases of fallen nests with young birds of prey, artificial platforms have been used as an emergency measure - adults desert the young if they remain on the ground. Artificial nest sites can also be used where a tree nest falls during winter gales for species like Hobby which tend to be faithful to a nest site. The broken, fallen nest may be replaced with an artificial one of the same size. Use the general technique described for Merlin but finish the nest with the same type of material as the original.

**Kestrel**                      *Falco tinnunculus*
Open Front                       300mm wide, 500mm deep, 300mm high. Front is
                                 150mm high.

The box should be mounted high, at least 5m above ground, sloping backwards slightly to keep eggs and young to the rear. The box should face, preferably, to the south east quarter and have a clear flight path to the entrance. Kestrel boxes have been used with great success in treeless areas, each box mounted on a pole fixed firmly in the ground. The pole must support both the box and the strain of a ladder and human. Pole mounted boxes may be as low as 3m from the ground. The pole may need to be sunk a metre or so deep to provide a firm enough support. Longer poles will require setting in concrete. Fix a perch along the top of the front (page 26). This perch should extend well to one side of the box to allow adults and young to sit alongside the box. Alternatively the box may have the entrance along the longer face. These boxes give less shelter but do allow young birds more perching room along the open edge.

Kestrels sometimes nest on platforms as described below for Merlins.

Nest: little or no material added, but hole may eventually become deep in prey remains and pellets. Eggs: 4-5, white appearing speckled reddish-brown. Incubation begins when the first or second egg is laid and so hatching is sequential. Young grow at different rates and frequently a smaller nestling dies before fledging. In years of poor food supply more than one young may fail to fledge.

**Merlin**                       *Falco columbarius*                  **Schedule 1**
Platform

Make a saucer shaped cup of 25mm mesh chicken wire about 500mm in diameter. Weave willow twigs into the wire to form a cup and line it with an inverted sod cut from nearby. Site the nests in pairs, one at a woodland edge close to where Crows are nesting and the other 10m to 20m away inside the wood. Alternatively nests can be sited in a shelter belt or in an isolated birch, pine or rowan near the headwater of a stream.

Nest: a bare hollow. Eggs: 5-6, pale buff with dense reddish markings. Incubation begins before the clutch is completed and hatching is sequential.

## Rails                                    *Rallidae*
Rafts and Islands with vegetation

Moorhen and Coot will take to almost any such site, Moorhen nesting on islands only 500mm in diameter. Moorhen often use open or hole entrance boxes provided for wildfowl.

Nest: large heaps of aquatic vegetation. Eggs: typically 6-10, off-white with brownish speckles, but very variable. Some large Moorhen clutches are laid by two females. Young remain in the nest for a few days after hatching. Other nest platforms are built as brooding or roosting sites for the young. Later broods of Moorhen may be fed by young from earlier broods.

## Waders                                        Some  **Schedule 1**

Waders generally nest in a shallow scrape on the ground. Scrapes are simply depressions in the ground large enough to take the eggs. Experienced birdwatchers develop a feel for the types of site where particular waders are able to dig out scrapes. Snipe, for instance, nest in a depression in the centre of a large tuft of grass or sedge, whereas Lapwings prefer to nest on the top of an undulation near a tuft. Scrapes may be made in older tufts of grass by clearing out the dead grass from the centre. Little Ringed Plover need a small depression in fresh bare shingle - gravel works often have suitable sites. Greenshank, Stone-curlew and various other waders like a clear marker such as a stump or large stone near the nest site. Sites which have no such markers may be enhanced by adding some. Waders such as Redshank, Snipe and Black-tailed Godwit nesting in grazed wet pasture can be assisted by the provision of fenced-off areas to prevent trampling by cattle. Remember to unfence these areas after the breeding season to allow the area to remain as the grazed habitat which these waders require.

## Kittiwake                          *Rissa tridactyla*
Platform

Kittiwakes have begun to nest on man-made sites in some places including the sides of coastal warehouses and piers. In these colonies, and probably in some natural colonies where nest sites are limited, ledges can be provided. Ledges should be about 300mm from front to back. However, the exact width of ledges is not critical since Kittiwake nests can adhere to almost anything and overhang a narrow ledge quite safely. If ledges are mounted above each other it is better to make higher ledges wider to help prevent lower ones becoming fouled by droppings. Ledges may be at any height provided they are safe from wave action at the highest of tides and in rough weather. Ledges may be any length from 300mm for a single nest to as long as the building allows. They should be sited, preferably, overhanging water. When considering new sites for Kittiwakes remember that their colonies are noisy and smelly and some people may not welcome them.

Nest: A firm cup of grass, mud and seaweed with a deep hollow centre. Eggs: 2, sometimes 3, blue-green to buff with brown blotches. Young remain in the nest for about 5 weeks.

## Roseate Tern                    *Sterna dougallii*                **Schedule 1**
Tunnel                         300mm square, 150mm high. Floorless.

Roseate Tern populations are under threat at present and it is possible that if suitable nest sites were available at other tern colonies they might begin nesting there. They require more concealed nesting sites than do Common Terns. Predation of nests and young by gulls, crows and Peregrines is a major threat to breeding success.

Nesting sites can be provided by allowing long rank vegetation to develop above the foreshore. Tree mallow (*Lavatera arborea*) has been planted in one reserve and used by these terns for nesting under.

In the USA old car tyres have been used successfully, although the presence of such 'rubbish' on otherwise 'natural' nature reserves might need explaining to some humans! Roseate Terns have also used wooden boxes for both nesting and shelter. Two types of box should be used. Both are 300mm square by 150mm high and floorless. The first, (page 24ii) used mainly as a shelter from the elements and predators by the young, has one side completely open. The second (page 24iii), used mainly as a nest chamber, has a 100mm wide open entrance the full height at the corner of one side.

Before attempting any work with Roseate Terns you should ask advice of the RSPB.

Nest: a hollow, practically unlined, on rock or among shingle or shore plants. Eggs: 1-2, creamy with variable amounts of dark marking.

## Common Tern                                           *Sterna hirundo*

Island, Raft or Platform

Islands should be clear of vegetation, covered only in shingle. Any plant growth may encourage Coots which will deter terns. The floor should be about 150mm above water level. Fence the edge to a height of 250mm with a fence strong enough not to be damaged by perching wildfowl. Allow about 0.5m² per pair of terns and ensure there are some markers such as stones for humans and birds to be able to identify territories and nests. Shelters may be used as for Roseate Terns.

Nest: a hollow on the ground, possibly lined with local materials. Eggs: 2-3, creamy with variable amounts of dark blotches.

## Little Tern                        *Sterna albifrons*                   Schedule 1

The main hazards to Little Terns, which nest only at coastal sites, are very high tides, human disturbance and predators. Various nest site creation techniques have been tried but all of them require time, effort and some are expensive in materials. Some have been very successful but artificial islands and the raising of areas of shingle beach using heavy earth moving equipment are expensive and generally ineffective in the long term because of rapid erosion by the sea.

Human disturbance can be partly combatted by wardening, notices and fences. Predation from the ground can be reduced by the use of electric fences. Little Terns often nest in sites accessible to walkers and holiday makers. If electric fences are used, due consideration must be given to the human population.

Before attempting any project with Little Terns, you must have appropriate licences for Schedule 1 birds and you should take advice from the RSPB who have experience of such techniques. For more details of the problems and methods see the booklet 'A guide to Little Tern Conservation' (RSPB).

Nest: a hollow, possibly lined with local materials. Eggs: 2-3, generally pale buff with dark blotches.

## Black Guillemot (Tystie)         *Cepphus grylle*

Tunnel and Chamber                   Square or round tunnel of height 120mm and length
                                     over 400mm. Chamber at least 300mm square and
                                     height 120mm.

The nest chamber should be as light-proof as possible but need not be buried in a heap of soil. The floor of the chamber should contain at least 100 flat pebbles or smooth gravel pieces less than 10mm in diameter in order for the adults to arrange a nesting scrape. The box can be placed near the shore or at a cliff base in an area free of ground predators and preferably with a suitable take-off platform nearby. Alternatively secure the box to a sea wall, pier or other fixed object about 2m above high water level. In this case a take-off platform about 300mm square should be attached at the tunnel entrance. Tunnels can be incorporated into sea walls under construction or repair. Tunnels need not be straight, but L-shaped, so may be made to fit inside fairly narrow structures. A suitable nest hole can also be made using flat stones or slabs. Black Guillemots are sensitive at the nest site.

Nest: normally an unlined scrape. Eggs: 2, whitish. Young fledge at about 35-40 days.

### Feral Pigeon

*Columba livia*

Hole Entrance

Medium. Entrance 100mm square. Landing platform or ledge below the entrance. Site at medium height.

Colony boxes with several chambers are acceptable.

Nest: loosely built of assorted materials, often with an accumulation of droppings. Eggs: 2, white. Breeding season may extend throughout the year.

### Stock Dove

*Columba oenas*

Hole Entrance Large

Entrance diameter 150mm. Site at upper medium height. Landing platform or ledge below the entrance.

The box should be placed in a tree or outbuilding near to open fields which have an ample supply of weed seeds. Stock Doves often nest amongst bales or in mangers within farm buildings. Suitable sites can be provided easily with owner's permission.

Stock Doves have several successive broods in one year. A later clutch of eggs may be laid before the present brood leave the nest. Droppings, which the adults do not clear from the nest, will foul these eggs and may prevent them from hatching (perhaps by making them impervious). Extra nestboxes may be sited nearby so that broods may be reared in alternate nest sites. If the inside of the box becomes wet, nestlings' feet may become cemented to the layer of slimy droppings. Check for this in wet weather or, better still, ensure the box is weather proof. Clean out the box at the end of the season (which may be in October or even November) leaving a fresh lining of wood bark.

Tawny Owls often use Stock Dove nests, laying their own clutch on top of the dove's nest and remains.

Nest: a thin layer of twigs, roots and other debris. A deep layer of droppings will accumulate during the season. Eggs: 2, white.

### Ring-necked Parakeet

*Psittacula krameri*

Hole Entrance

250mm square base and 800mm deep. Entrance hole 80mm diameter. Site at medium height or higher in a tree or on a building.

There are now a number of feral populations of this introduced species. Boxes should be made of thick wood to provide adequate insulation and should be thoroughly weatherproof. Ensure the box is relatively narrow and high. Nail some pieces of rough wood inside the box for the nesting birds to gnaw - this will make the box itself last longer! Ensure the inside of the box is of rough wood to allow young to cling to it. Ring-necked Parakeets breed early so ensure the box is in place before mid-winter. Line the bottom with bark chippings or shavings.

Nest: none or a shallow scrape in the debris on the nesting chamber floor. Eggs. 3-5, white.

**Barn Owl**
Hole Entrance

*Tyto alba*
At least 450mm wide, 450mm high and 750mm
deep. Entrance at least 150mm wide by 200mm high.

**Schedule 1**

There is no limit to the size of box which will suit Barn Owls: the bigger the better. The entrance should be half way up the front end. If possible make an extended floor in front of the box for young owls to exercise on.

Boxes may be sited inside buildings, in trees, on poles or in straw stacks. Barn Owls need nesting and roosting sites so two boxes in one territory will be helpful.

**In buildings.** Any large box - tea chest or packing case perhaps - will do. The box should be fixed to a wall or beam by strong brackets. If the box is on a beam ensure cats cannot get to it. Thorny twigs tied to the beam can help keep them off. Alternatively a whole section of the gable end of a floored loft can be blocked off from the main building leaving an 'owl loft'. If the box is in a building used for storing foodstuffs ensure the birds cannot contaminate the foods. This can be done by fixing the box with its entrance butting up to the entrance hole in the wall of the building.

**In trees.** Owls will nest in large tree holes. Isolated tall broken stumps are very suitable sites for boxes. These boxes must have a landing platform or have the entrance opening on to a broad branch. Boxes in trees must be thoroughly weather proofed and face south-east away from prevailing winds. Exterior boxes should have an interior baffle running ½ to ¾ of the distance from front to back and reaching ¾ of the way to the roof (page 22 ii). This gives extra seclusion and shelter to the birds whilst still allowing adequate ventilation in the nesting chamber. The cutting diagram in the appendix gives a design for a tree mounted box which can be made from an 8' x 4' sheet of exterior plywood.

**On poles.** These are identical to tree boxes sited as for the pole-mounted Kestrel box. Clearly the pole must be very strong and secure to support the weight of the box, birds and accumulating layer of pellets. Poles may be sited on treeless farmland at intersections of ditches and drains. These boxes are very obvious and their installation requires heavy equipment. It is of little use trying this design unless it is as part of an overall habitat management programme. The Hawk and Owl Trust are happy to offer advice on such projects.

**In stacks.** A box may be constructed the size and shape of a standard bale - 900mm long, 450mm high and 350mm wide. The box should be sited in a stack as it is being built. Two of these boxes may be placed at opposite ends of one stack allowing both Kestrel and Barn Owl to nest.

Barn Owls are sensitive to disturbance at all times so boxes should be sited in places with the minimum possible disturbance. The owls must have constant access to the box. A hole in a wall is better than leaving a window or door open. Boxes should be sited in locations away from busy roads. Barn Owls which hunt along roads are very vulnerable to collision with traffic. Boxes are best put up on the edge of existing Barn Owl strongholds - local knowledge is useful here. The height of boxes is of little importance to the owls themselves. The main consideration is interference by humans and predation. Typical minimum workable heights are about 5m in trees or 3.5m on poles. Boxes should be cleaned every year or two leaving just a thin layer of pellets over the floor. New boxes should be lined with bark chippings.

Nest: none or a hollow in the floor of the cavity. Eggs: 4-7, white. Eggs hatch sequentially, younger and smaller nestlings may be eaten by the older ones in years of poor food supply.

**Little Owl**
Hole Entrance
Chimney

*Athene noctua*
Large, entrance diameter 70mm.
800mm long, diameter 200mm, entrance diameter 70mm. Site at medium height.

Little Owls do not take readily to boxes in this country probably because they are able to utilise a much wider range of natural holes than the other larger owls. In areas where even smallish holes are scarce, nestboxes may be used more often. They prefer dark hidden cavities for nest chambers, so make boxes as light-proof as possible. An internal baffle in a hole entrance box may be used. Chimney boxes should be attached either below or above a nearly horizontal branch. A deep nesting chamber can be built at the end of a chimney box, the structure looking like a hanging inverted tunnel and chamber. A perch, sheltered by the roof overhang, should be fitted to allow the male to sit at the entrance whilst the female incubates the eggs. The floor should be covered in bark chippings, arranged to give a horizontal surface whatever the actual angle of the floor of the box. The entrance diameter is important - any larger size would allow Tawny Owls to enter and drive out the intended occupants. The box may be sited at any height provided it is free from predation and interference from humans or grazing cattle.

Nest: no material added. Eggs: 3-5, white. Eggs hatch almost at the same time. Young leave the nest together, sometimes before being able to fly freely.

**Tawny Owl**
Chimney
Hole Entrance

*Strix aluco*
800mm long, 250mm square, open at one end.
Large/Very Large, up to 1m deep, entrance 150mm square.

Tawny Owls nest readily in boxes. Some populations seem to prefer the chimney box, others only take a more traditional hole entrance box and the rest will take either. If in doubt try a variety of designs to start with and then concentrate on the successful types. Chimney boxes, which mimic a hole in the end of a broken off branch, may be fixed in several ways but should in any case be steeper than 45° to the horizontal. Hole entrance boxes may be just like an oversize tit box. Alternatively, try a relatively deeper box with the same dimensions as the chimney but with the entrance a large hole at the top of one of the vertical sides. With deep boxes ensure the inside surface is rough enough for young owls to climb out. Occasionally Tawny Owls may take old crow nests or platforms put out for other birds. Plastic barrels in trees have been used successfully in some places.

The height of the nest is of little importance to the owls provided the box is free of disturbance, particularly by humans. It is unlikely that a site below 2.5m would be suitable.

Boxes are best sited early in the year in Tawny Owl territories. A January night visit will reveal the location of their territories. Clean the boxes after the owls fledge. The nests are often a productive source of bird rings. Tawny Owls are sensitive to disturbance early in the season and are always dangerous if approached carelessly. Always wear goggles, and preferably a safety helmet, as protection from talon attack

Tawny Owl chicks leave the nest before they are able to fly freely and spend some days hiding amongst branches. They are sometimes found, apparently helpless, on the ground. (Chicks of other owls and raptors may occasionally be found like this too). In these cases it is best to place the chick as high as you can reach in the nearest bush, well out of the way of dogs and children. You should never assume it is abandoned and in need of human foster parents.

Nest: no material added but a scrape may be made in the base of the cavity. Eggs: 2-5, white. Young hatch sequentially and smaller birds will fail to survive in years of poor food supply.

**Long-eared Owl**                    *Asio otus*
Platform

The normal nest site is an old nest of a Crow, Magpie or Woodpigeon usually in a copse, shelter belt or plantation.

The most suitable nest is a circular wicker basket 300-400mm in diameter and 150-200mm deep with nearly vertical sides. Hardware stores and garden centres often have a range of baskets, some of which will be suitable. (There may be professional basket makers locally, but if not why not try persuading an amateur basket maker or a school or college art and craft department to do their bit for conservation?) Baskets will last longer if they are varnished before use.

Long-eared Owls are often associated with conifers although any tree which gives adequate overhead shelter is suitable - particularly birch, willow or thorny scrub. Tie or wire the basket in the chosen tree at a height of 4m or above. The wire or cord should be tied to the base of the basket so that it will be hidden after the basket is lined. Once the box is fixed, line it to just under half its depth with dead twigs. Sawdust, shavings and the like are unsuitable for lining these nests as they may become waterlogged in wet weather. Baskets may be spaced as close as 100m apart.

Long-eared Owls often cannot compete with Tawny Owls although it still may be worth placing boxes for both species in an area where both species are present.

Nest: no material added. Eggs: 3-5, white. Eggs hatch sequentially. Youngest owl often fails to fledge.

**Nightjar**                    *Caprimulgus europaeus*
Platform

Create a bare patch in extensive tracts of heather or bracken exposing sand or peat. This simulates the favoured charcoal burner's sites often used in past. The bare patch is best in the shade of a bushy shrub 1-3m tall. It should be roughly elliptical, about 1m wide and stretching about 1.5m from the base of the shrub northwards. The bare patch will need to be cleared of weeds annually. Alternatively try a platform made of a cross section of tree trunk 300mm in diameter and 80mm thick placed on the ground.

Nest: an unlined scrape. Eggs: 2, cream with darker blotches.

**Swift**                    *Apus apus*
Hole Entrance                    600mm deep, 130mm wide, 100mm high. Entrance at one end of the box or under one end. Entrance hole should be either a slit 30mm wide or segment of circle width at widest part 30mm. An entrance template is given on page 40.

Site as high as possible, under the eaves of a house or within a loft with just the entrance hole protruding through the wall. Swifts will take to holes with a vertical access but these are easier for House Sparrows and Starlings to use, so the horizontal entrance illustrated on page 22 is preferable if there may be competition for the box. The shape of the box is not important. They may be made with a right angled bend in them to fit around corners of houses. If it is possible make the nesting chamber at the far end of the box wider and a little higher than the tunnel of the box. A ring of plaited straw at the back end of the box to act as a base for the nest may help to attract Swifts. Marley have developed a roof tile, with an entrance, behind which Swifts can nest.

Swifts are sensitive to disturbance and must not be handled in the nestbox. There is no need to position boxes until just before the Swifts arrive: this helps deter sparrows. Clean the boxes after use. Swift nests may contain many large parasites. Box entrances may be plugged after

Swifts have departed to keep out other birds over the winter and early spring. Remember to unplug them before the Swifts return!

Nest: a cup of plant material collected on the wing and cemented with saliva. Eggs: 2-3, dull white. Incubation period of about 20 days and fledging period of 5 weeks may be prolonged in cold and wet weather. In these conditions young may become cold and semi-torpid and may remain unbrooded for over 24 hours.

| **Kingfisher** | *Alcedo atthis* | **Schedule 1** |
|---|---|---|
| Tunnel | 700mm long, 50mm diameter, chamber 200mm long and 120mm high. | |

Nesting sites may limit Kingfisher breeding populations in areas where there are no suitable vertical banks or where the bank material is unsuitable for excavation, perhaps because of large stones. In the absence of a vertical bank one may be cut. This operation is much simpler bordering large ponds or lakes than in streams or rivers where erosion by running water may be a problem. Once the vertical wall is cut, tunnels may be incorporated.

Bore a tunnel in a vertical or steeply sloping, preferably north-east facing, bank. The tunnel entrance should be in a clear face of bank with no overhang, obstructions, cracks or roots nearer than about a metre. Any of these would allow mammalian predators easy access. The tunnel should be wider than it is high and must slope upwards at about 15° to horizontal, starting at least 1m above the highest flood water level. The entrance should, if possible, be at least 300mm below the top of the bank to prevent collapse or predators digging down. Fibreglass nest chambers are more predator resistant and can be safely placed nearer the surface. Alternatively bore an oversize hole and insert a precast concrete or fibreglass floorless tunnel and chamber into the hole. Push the entrance end of the tunnel 100mm behind the bank face. This will both help camouflage and prevent it from sticking out if there is a small earth fall. Refill the chamber and the rear part of the tunnel with soil.

Sometimes Kingfishers may abandon a tunnel during excavation on striking some big obstacle such as a stone. In these cases it is possible to remove the obstacle and perhaps install an artificial nesting chamber at the end of this otherwise natural tunnel.

If there are no convenient perches nearby fix one or two sticks or branches projecting from the bank. There are also opportunities for tunnels in artificially constructed banks or in stone and concrete walls. Tunnels may be sited about a metre apart to allow for more than one brood by the same pair.

Kingfishers are very sensitive to disturbance especially early in the nesting cycle. Inspection is best done from a distance.

Nest: no material added, but fish bones collect through the season. Eggs: 6-10, white. Two, sometimes three, broods.

| **Wryneck** | *Jynx torquilla* | **Schedule 1** |
|---|---|---|
| Hole Entrance | Medium, entrance hole elliptical, 45mm high and 35mm wide. | |

It may be preferable to make a concave base to the box. Budgerigar nestbox bases are suitable, white polystyrene foam can be cut to shape easily.

Nest: no material added to cavity. Old material may be ejected. Eggs: 7-10, white.

## Woodpeckers

Boxes should be filled with polystyrene foam or substitute except behind the entrance hole.

Nests: no lining material added to cavity.

**Green Woodpecker**                    *Picus viridis*

Hole Entrance, filled                   450mm high, 180mm square base. Entrance diameter 60mm.

    Place the box high on a tree trunk.

Eggs: 5-7, white.


**Great Spotted Woodpecker**            *Dendrocopos major*

Hole Entrance, filled                   400mm high, 140mm square base. Entrance diameter 50mm.

    Place the box high on a tree trunk in a very secluded place.

Eggs: 4-7, white.


**Lesser Spotted Woodpecker**           *Dendrocopos minor*

Hole Entrance, filled                   Medium, Entrance diameter 32mm.

    Place box at medium height or higher, on the underside of a steeply angled branch.

Eggs: 4-6, white.


**Ground Nesting Songbirds**

    Skylark, Yellow Wagtail and Meadow Pipit have been encouraged to nest in particular sites by improving then to mimic the most favoured natural ones used by the species. In most cases there will be so many potential natural sites available that such improvement is unnecessary. However, enthusiasts studying the species may find this a useful technique to encourage birds to nest where they wish them to, particularly in large areas of uniform vegetation such as grass or heather. One possible site improvement is to clear the centre of a small tussock of grass to make a nesting space for Skylarks.


**Sand Martin**                         *Riparia riparia*

Tunnel filled with sand                 Up to 1000mm long, 100mm diameter.

    Arrange several earthenware pipes filled with sand in a natural or artificial sandbank. The pipes should preferably be at least 350mm below the bank top and at least 350mm above its base. An artificial bank can be constructed from rubble with a cement facing. Only the pipes themselves will be excavatable by the birds. Loosen the sand at the entrance to the pipe to show the birds where to burrow, but ensure that sand inside the pipe is still easily visible from outside. The pipes should slope very gently down to the entrance to allow for drainage. The bank should be vertical or overhanging slightly. Plant the top with overhanging vegetation. Where tunnels are made in an artificial bank, place a ball of hard packed sand at the far end of the pipe so that the birds can excavate a nesting chamber of greater diameter than the rest of the tunnel. Ensure that the rubble above this sand will not collapse when the sand is excavated. Pipes should not protrude beyond the bank face.

    One very successful artificial site was created in a canal bank faced with sheet steel piling. Circular holes cut in the piling formed the entrances to the clay piping tunnels behind. Occasionally Sand Martins have nested in freshly dumped piles of wettish but firm sand. It may be worth leaving such heaps of sand for them. Sheets of corrugated iron separated by a 200mm depth of sand in such heaps will keep the nests free of rain water and also prevent the tunnel roof from collapse. The sheets should slope slightly downwards to the tunnel entrances for drainage. It will be worthwhile digging a few beginnings of tunnels.

    In natural banks, Sand Martins can be attracted to nest by starting holes with a trowel. This is useful in places like sand quarries where certain banks are only safe for a season and others are to be removed. Each spring, clean out the artificial burrows and repack them with fresh sand. Inspection of these nests can only be made if a hatch is made in the rear of the pipes or with an endoscope. This is possible if the whole nesting colony is built within a metre-wide artificial bank.

Nest: lined with plant material and feathers. Eggs: 4-5, white.

## Swallow                    *Hirundo rustica*
Platform

Site platforms singly inside outbuildings against beams or walls. Ensure the site has continuous access. Swallows may build a nest on a base as small as a single nail projecting from a wall, but it is better to provide something more substantial. The two chamber platform illustrated (page 35) has a height of 150mm and each platform is 100mm square. As with House Martins, provide muddy puddles if needed.

Nest: lined with feathers. Eggs: 4-6, white. Young return to roost at the nest after fledging. Usually 2 or 3 broods.

## House Martin               *Delichon urbica*
Hole Entrance, special design          Internal dimensions 70mm high, 120mm wide at back, 90mm deep. An entrance hole template is given in page 40.

Mount the box under the eaves of a house at medium height. If the house lacks eaves, a ledge about 120mm wide can be fitted to the wall and boxes secured underneath. Ensure that eaves and ledges do not allow water to trickle into the nests. If possible site boxes in a group rather than singly. Boxes may attract a new colony of House Martins, even if the artificial boxes are not themselves used.

Inspection is best done using a dentist's mirror. Ringing of nestlings can be either through a hatch in the ledge above, or by removing the nest. Various arrangements for removing the nest safely are workable. The box and backing plate can slide out, or the box be unscrewed from the ledge. For this, wing nuts are convenient. (Carry a spare!)

In places where natural supplies of building material are scarce provide a shallow muddy puddle about 1m wide. The mud should be a mixture including soil, lime, clay and cow dung. To help clay adhere to smooth walls fix to the wall a 20mm wide ledge 100mm below the eaves. Between the ledge and eaves attach small-mesh wire netting. An artificial House Martin nest adjacent to this ledge may encourage a new colony.

Natural and artificial nests can be taken over by House Sparrows which may enlarge entrances after the martins have left. Entrance holes of natural nests may be armoured against attacks in the autumn using cement. Both natural and artificial nests could have their entrances plugged until the following spring (but ensure your Wrens are not deprived of a good winter roosting site). Artificial nests can be taken down during the winter months. (This also helps prolong the life of papier mâché boxes.)

Nest: lined with feathers and vegetable matter. Eggs: 4-5, white. Young of earlier broods may help feed later young. Young may use the nest for roosting after fledging.

## Grey Wagtail               *Motacilla cinerea*
Open Fronted                  Medium, mounted low.

Site the box immediately above a swiftly flowing stream underneath some natural or man-made overhang such as ivy or a bridge. The box should be hidden from sight from the bank above but have a clear outlook over the water. It should be at least 1m above the flood-water level.

Boxes will be exposed to the wet throughout their lives so it is worthwhile using galvanized nails and marine ply or tanalised wood. Joints at the top and back should be made with watertight joints but with drainage holes in the base.

Nest: of twigs, roots, moss and leaves, lined with hair. Eggs: 4-6, pale buff, finely speckled.

## Pied Wagtail
Open Fronted

*Motacilla alba*
Small.

Site boxes at low or medium height. Pied Wagtails will take boxes in a variety of situations - walls overlooking lawns, on beams or on machinery in farm outbuildings, under bridges as for Grey Wagtail and anywhere on sewage farms (where boxes may be placed fairly close together).

Nest: of twigs, roots and moss, lined with locally available material. Eggs: 5-6, greyish, speckled brown.

## Dipper
Open fronted

*Cinclus cinclus*
Medium.

Dipper and Grey Wagtail nest in similar sites, the former preferring cavities with a lower front sill. Both species will take boxes placed for the other and it is worthwhile putting two boxes on structures such as bridges where both species occur. As with Grey Wagtail, boxes need to be made with wetness in mind. Boxes for Dippers have been particularly valuable where older stone, wood or brick built structures have been replaced by concrete ones with few, if any, possible nesting cavities. They have also enabled Dipper populations to increase along rivers (in Britain, Europe and USA) where there are few natural sites.

The front of the box can be very low or even absent, making the box a mere platform. Site the box by water under a bridge or concealed in the bank by overgrowth or other natural features. Boxes can be built into the walls of new bridges by leaving out a brick or building block during construction. Dippers have sometimes nested in tunnels such as drainage pipes although a purpose-built rectangular cavity is far better than a round tunnel.

Nest: a domed structure of moss and grass, lined with dead leaves. Eggs: 4-5, white.

## Wren
Open Fronted



Hole entrance

*Troglodytes troglodytes*
Small/Very Small with a high front leaving only a 30mm high entrance slit.
Size as above, with hole diameter 30mm or more.

Wrens will take to many sorts of holes. For the open fronted box it is preferable to make the lid removable for inspection and cleaning. Wrens will take to larger boxes but there is little point in making boxes larger as the Wrens only have to bring in more nest material. Mount the box low down preferably fairly well hidden in thick undergrowth. Boxes can be set into the bank of a stream, preferably under an overhang of roots below the bank top.

The male Wren builds several unlined 'cock nests', then the female selects one and lines it with feathers. If you have one such cock nest it is worth putting up 2 or 3 more boxes in similar sites several metres away from the first. The male is fairly likely to select one of these for a later nest since he is already a box user. At the end of the season remove all but one of these boxes in order to have a supply of extra ones ready for the next season.

Clean the nest immediately after fledging to cater for a possible second brood. Each brood is brought up in a fresh nest. Do not empty boxes of unused 'cock nests' until August. The female may use one of these for a late brood even after it has been standing empty for several weeks or months.

Nest: a domed structure of leaves, moss and grass. Normally close inspection of the interior of a Wren nest is not possible without damaging the nest. However, nests in boxes can often be inspected with care since the box prevents the nest from falling apart. Eggs: 5-6, white.

**Open Nesting Songbirds**
Nest Bundles

This category potentially includes all songbirds which nest off the ground in bushes and shrubs although Blackbird (which may also take to assorted platforms and ledges) and Song Thrush will possibly be the chief users of these sites. Bundles of vegetation (page 37) can be placed anywhere in suitable habitats. Gardens, newly coppiced woodland and conifer plantations are places where these nest sites will be of value. Bundles made of evergreen branches will be of greater value early in the season before deciduous plants come into full leaf.

| **Robin** | *Erithacus rubecula* | |
|---|---|---|
| Open Fronted | Small. | |

Robins are small scale but regular nestbox users. Mount the box low in a well hidden site, camouflaged by climbing plants and preferably protected by thorny shrubbery.
Nest: a large cup of leaves, grass and moss lined with roots or hairs. The nest may be domed when built in some enclosed spaces. Eggs: 5-6, white with a variable amount of speckles.

| **Black Redstart** | *Phoenicurus ochruros* | **Schedule 1** |
|---|---|---|
| Open Fronted | Small. | |

A good alternative to a box is a ledge in a large shed or building, high under the roof. Make sure there is a good free access and plenty of other smaller escape holes. Although this is a scarce nesting species, it is worth placing boxes where singing males are found in spring.
Nest: a cup of grass, stems and moss lined with wool or hair. Eggs: 4-6, white.

| **Redstart** | *Phoenicurus phoenicurus* |
|---|---|
| Hole Entrance | Long box, 100mm wide, 250mm deep and 130mm high with entrance hole diameter 35mm and a low partition across the floor of the box. |
| or | Medium, entrance diameter 35mm. |
| or | 300mm wide, 150mm deep and 150mm high with a 75mm square entrance at the top of one end of a longer side (page 24i). |
| Open Fronted | Medium, front coming up to 40mm below roof. |

Redstarts take to a variety of boxes, but in certain localities they seem only to take one type of box. The common features of these boxes are that they are larger than normal tit boxes with a larger entrance hole and possibly have a darker nesting chamber. Try them all and concentrate on the one that works in your area. If they do not work, try modifications. For the open fronted box, a removable lid will assist inspection. A narrow landing ledge below the hole may be of assistance. Site the box at medium height on the edge of woodland, preferably on an oak. Ensure there are plenty of song posts nearby.

Redstarts suffer from competition from almost all other hole nesting birds. Possibly the main problem is to find a design that Redstarts are happy with but that the opposition (Pied Flycatchers, Blue Tits etc.) do not like. Redstarts are sensitive to disturbance.
Nest: of dead grass, moss, roots or bark lined with hair and feathers. Eggs: 6-7, light blue.

| **Wheatear** | *Oenanthe oenanthe* |
|---|---|
| Tunnel | 100mm square , 800mm long. |

Position the tunnel in a gently sloping bank or bury it in a pile of shingle. Cover the floor with shingle. The tunnel entrance should be only about 50mm wide. Either partially close the entrance with a stone or fit a front to the tunnel with a 50mm diameter hole. Some workers have had success using a jerrycan as the chamber (with an enlarged entrance) and a tunnel roofed over with corrugated iron, the entire system covered in shingle.

If an inspection hatch is built into the tunnel, bear in mind that Wheatears often build the nest about two-thirds of the way down the tunnel rather than at the far end.

Wheatears need some perches along the approach path to the box. Twigs stuck in the ground or boulders will do.

Nest: a heap of grass, moss, roots and leaves lined with grass, hair, wool or feathers. Eggs: 5-6, pale blue.

**Spotted Flycatcher**     *Muscicapa striata*
Open Fronted     150mm wide, 100mm high, 100mm deep. Front
     rising only 25mm above floor. Set at medium height.
Platform

Spotted Flycatchers like a nest site with a clear outlook but shelter above. Any artificial site needs only a very low front whose function is just to retain the nest. It is worth trying boxes with open sides as well as an open front. In a situation where there is already shelter above (under low eaves for example) the box need be only a platform with retaining edges. Site the box with a good outlook - the edge of a glade or overlooking a lawn are suitable positions. A missing brick in a wall screened by climbing plants is often a good nest site. The box itself can be well hidden provided that there is a clear view from it. A wall covered in ivy or honeysuckle is often a good site. The nest is very vulnerable to predation, so a wire balloon over the front is worthwhile. Make sure there is a perch nearby - a stick in the ground a couple of metres from the box will do.

Nest: a tiny cup of miscellaneous material including spiders webs, lined with feathers and leaves. Eggs: 4-5, off-white, usually mottled reddish. The nestling period of about two weeks is often prolonged in cold and wet weather.

**Pied Flycatcher**     *Ficedula hypoleuca*
Hole Entrance     Small/Medium, entrance diameter 28mm.

Set the box at medium height, preferably overlooking a woodland glade or in a wood with little undergrowth. Ensure there is a suitable perch within a couple of metres of the box and that there is a clear approach to this perch. If competition with tits is a problem, boxes can be mounted in small clusters. Tits will not nest very close to each other, leaving boxes free for Pied Flycatchers. As a cheaper alternative holes may be blocked with a cork until the flycatchers arrive, by which time most titmice will be be incubating.

Nest: a large cup of leaves, grass, bark, moss and lichen lined with hair, grass and possibly wool or feathers. Eggs: 4-7, pale blue.

**Tits**

Nests: all hole-nesting tits (except the Willow Tit and sometimes the Crested Tit) have nests of moss lined with local material in an existing hole. In a particular place the variation between the nests of the various species is less than that within one species. The materials used will be those immediately available. Eggs: all white with a variable amount of speckling, usually more at one end than at the other. All tits will cover their eggs, sometimes very deeply, in lining material when they are off the nest. Inspect them with care, particularly during egg laying.

**Marsh Tit**     *Parus palustris*
Hole Entrance     Small, entrance diameter 25mm.

Site the box low. Marsh Tits may lose in competition for boxes with other tits. To avoid

this, boxes should be placed more densely than the other tits can manage to fill. Marsh Tits are regular but rather infrequent box users.
Eggs: 6-9.

**Willow Tit**                     *Parus montanus*
Hole Entrance, filled              Small, entrance diameter 25mm.
    Site the box low down in thick cover. Wood shavings will probably be a suitable alternative filling to polystyrene. To attract Willow Tits to an area, strap rotting birch logs to sound tree trunks - naturally excavated nests cannot be inspected without a small mirror or endoscope. Colonisation of a new area is more likely if there are existing populations nearby, for Willow Tits are very sedentary. Other tits may oust Willow Tits from their newly excavated nest holes.
Nest: often only with a lining of wood fibres but sometimes of moss and feathers. Eggs: 6-9.

**Crested Tit**                    *Parus cristatus*                    **Schedule 1**
Hole Entrance, filled              Small, entrance diameter 28mm.
    Site the box at medium height. Success with these birds has been variable and it may take a few years for a particular population to take to boxes. Some birds will nest in unfilled hole entrance boxes.
Nest: a typical tit nest inside the excavated cavity; the lining may include spiders' webs. Eggs: 4-8.

**Coal Tit**                       *Parus ater*
Hole Entrance                      Small, entrance diameter 25mm.
    Site the box low. In a deciduous woodland an isolated conifer tree may be a productive place for a box. Some people have had success using a box with the entrance in the roof and placed on the ground.
Nest: usually neater than that of a Blue Tit and may include spiders' webs. Eggs 7-9.

**Blue Tit**                       *Parus caeruleus*
Hole Entrance                      Small, entrance diameter 25mm.
    Site the box at medium height anywhere in a suitable habitat. Blue Tits are our most reliable nestbox users. In periods of cold and wet weather Blue and Great Tits may suspend laying for a few days and restart when better weather returns.
Nest: Usually of moss lined with feathers. Eggs: 7-12.

**Great Tit**                      *Parus major*
Hole Entrance                      Medium, entrance diameter 28mm.
    Set the box at medium height anywhere in a suitable habitat. Great Tits will benefit from larger boxes than the other tits. If Tree Sparrows oust Great Tits, make boxes very deep (up to 500mm) for Great Tits. Tree Sparrows will use the shallower boxes and Great Tit the deeper ones. Great Tits prefer smaller cavities for roosting in winter. If the Great Tit boxes are large, ensure there are some smaller boxes with a 28mm entrance hole to allow these tits a roosting site.
Nest: often very bulky and the base may include twigs or roots. Eggs: 8-13, typically larger than those of the other tits. Sometimes eggs are laid in the moss before the lining is completed.

**Nuthatch**                                  *Sitta europaea*
Hole Entrance                                 Medium, entrance diameter 32mm.
   Mount the box at the upper end of the medium height range.
Nest: mud plastered around the entrance, sides and roof of the nest cavity. The floor is lined with wood chippings and leaves. When inspecting take care not to let mud fall from the roof on to the eggs. Eggs: 6-9, white, variably speckled reddish. Well-grown nestlings may be sexed by flank colour.


**Treecreeper**                               *Certhia familiaris*
Natural Site Improvement
   There is little problem in getting Treecreepers to nest in artificial sites. The main difficulty is in making a site which is easy to inspect and ring the young. Various inspectable designs (including the often quoted wedge) have been developed for Treecreepers but have met with little consistent success.
   Treecreepers will nest between two pieces of wood - an easy way of achieving this is to fix a strip of bark over a concavity in a tree trunk. The cavity behind the bark should be about 70mm wide and 100mm high with a distance of 30mm between bark and tree trunk. Entrances are from either side of the bark strip. Select a rough barked tree and set these bark sites in groups of three or four with the groups spaced out 200m or so apart. Clefts in trees can be utilised for siting a 'cabin' made out of three pieces of bark (page 38). In any design, there must be two entrances adjacent to the tree trunk, one on each side of the box.
   It may be possible to arrange two pieces of timber with bark attached against a trunk. This design will look like an open book facing the trunk. An inspection hatch can be made in the top or sides. Entrance will be through gaps at either side. Two such designs which have been successful in Scandinavia are illustrated (page 38). Boxes should be placed at heights between 1m and 3m. Treecreepers are sensitive to disturbance.
Nest: a cup of twigs, roots, grass and moss lined with feathers, bark and wool. Eggs: 6, white, finely speckled reddish.


**Jackdaw**                                   *Corvus monedula*
Hole Entrance                                 Large, entrance diameter 150mm.
   Mount the box high. Jackdaws are generally secretive and need to be able to enter the box inconspicuously.
Nest: of sticks, lined with wool, hair or various other materials. In small holes there may be no twigs but in very large holes great quantities of sticks are used. Eggs: 4-6, pale blue with some darker speckles.


**Starling**                                  *Sturnus vulgaris*
Hole Entrance                                 Medium to large, entrance diameter 45mm sited at
                                              medium height.
   Starlings will take almost any available cavity but generally success is greater in larger holes. They prefer a deep box mounted higher rather than lower. In spite of their aggressive behaviour they are sensitive to disturbance at the nest. They may nest colonially and several boxes can be placed close together.
Nest: a heap of plant material, lined with feathers, moss and wool. In traditional sites the nest may be many layers deep. Eggs: 4-7, light blue. The occasional Starling egg found on the ground near a nest is probably one removed by another Starling which has laid its own egg in place of this evicted one.

**House Sparrow**  
Hole Entrance

*Passer domesticus*  
Medium, entrance diameter 32mm set at medium height.

House Sparrows will take almost any cavity with a large enough entrance hole. Like Tree Sparrows they are sensitive to disturbance.

Nest: an untidy domed structure of almost any material available, but occasionally a cup only. Lined with feathers, hair and wool. Eggs: 3-5, whitish or pale blue with darker spots.

**Tree Sparrow**  
Hole Entrance

*Passer montanus*  
Small/medium, entrance diameter 28mm.

Tree Sparrows are very sensitive to disturbance and should be treated with great caution. They are relatively easy to attract to nestboxes which can be placed quite close to each other. They usually colonise an area fairly quickly but after three or four years the nestbox colony may dwindle to almost nothing. Some workers have suggested siting a second batch of boxes in a loosely spaced group some distance away from the original colony as it begins to decrease. Nesting sites are selected well before the breeding season proper, sometimes in the previous autumn, and the nests are built some time before eggs are laid. Laying is usually preceded by the appearance of freshly picked small leaves in the nest. There is much to be learned about Tree Sparrow population dynamics and breeding behaviour, their unusual sensitivity making investigation difficult.

Tree Sparrows raise up to three broods in a year. Smaller boxes tend to hold fewer consecutive broods in any year. Removing the very foul nest after a brood has fledged will cause the parents to nest elsewhere, so boxes should not be cleaned out until after the protracted nesting season is over. Tree Sparrows use the nest for winter roosting.

Nest: an untidy domed structure of dry grasses lined with feathers. Eggs: 4-6, whitish with brown blotches or speckles. The eggs tend to be smaller, browner and more rounded than those of House Sparrow.

# PREDATORS, PARASITES AND OTHER USERS

## PREDATORS

Predators may take eggs, chicks or even the incubating bird from nestboxes. Generally, only a small proportion of boxes is affected but sometimes predators learn that nestboxes provide an easy meal and they may then systematically work their way round many boxes. It is often difficult or illegal to remove predators but some preventive measures can be taken. They may be expensive or time-consuming, but one simple technique is to make boxes of a variety of designs. This makes it more difficult for predators to learn that these unnatural objects in trees are food sources but it also makes it more difficult for birds to learn that they are nest sites.

### Ground Nests

Some important tern colonies have been protected from foxes by electric fencing. When contemplating electric fencing remember responsibility towards humans who may be, quite legally, in the area and stumble across the fence. Fences erected on bad conductors (e.g. shingle) need both live and earth wires. More information is included in 'A guide to Little Tern conservation' (see Appendix). Remove rats or mink from islands by trapping but ensure that protected animals, such as otters, can be released unharmed.

Nests in natural sites on the ground may be protected using a dome made from 40mm mesh chicken wire placed over the nest. This size of wire works for birds smaller than thrushes. A canopy of wire placed above nests of thrushes or Blackbirds will help to keep Magpies off. It is also possible to protect natural nests in bushes in a similar way, but *read the note under Inspection and Recording before you attempt these methods.*

### Tree Nests

All British mammals can be kept away from nestboxes to some extent by making access difficult. The safest method is to hang boxes from branches with an anti-climbing cone around a slippery wire. Hanging boxes are available from the German company Schwegler. Trunk-mounted boxes can be protected with a pair of collars around the trunk above and below the box. These collars should be of tough polythene for protection against small mammals or of sheet metal against larger ones. Alternatively use gorse or briar collars. Such measures are pointless if the box is mounted where it can be reached by a single jump from the ground or a nearby branch. 'Gas pipe' boxes made of thick plastic are fairly resistant to squirrels.

Another approach is to make a slippery box on which the predator is unable cling. A covering of plastic, formica or metal helps but grey squirrels can gnaw through formica and plastic once they gain a foothold. A roof covering with a flexible projection over the entrance hole will deposit predators on the ground below as it bends under their weight. Such coverings also add to the weather proofing of boxes. Prickly twigs on the roof help to deter cats.

The entry of mammals is hampered by fixing a wide angled funnel over the entrance or a short length of tubing into the entrance hole. Some workers have suggested this reduces the desirability of boxes to birds: it certainly makes them more conspicuous to humans. Entry of the limbs of larger mammals is made ineffective by using deep boxes with high entrance holes (although sometimes tits will fill a deep box with nesting material nearly to the top). It helps to make the hole as near to the roof as possible and allow the roof a longer overhang. This makes access by predators from the roof more difficult. Bore the entrance hole sloping upwards, again making reaching down into the box by predators more difficult. A ledge placed just inside of the entrance hole allows nestlings to hide where marauding mammals cannot reach. Some

# KEEPING PREDATORS OFF

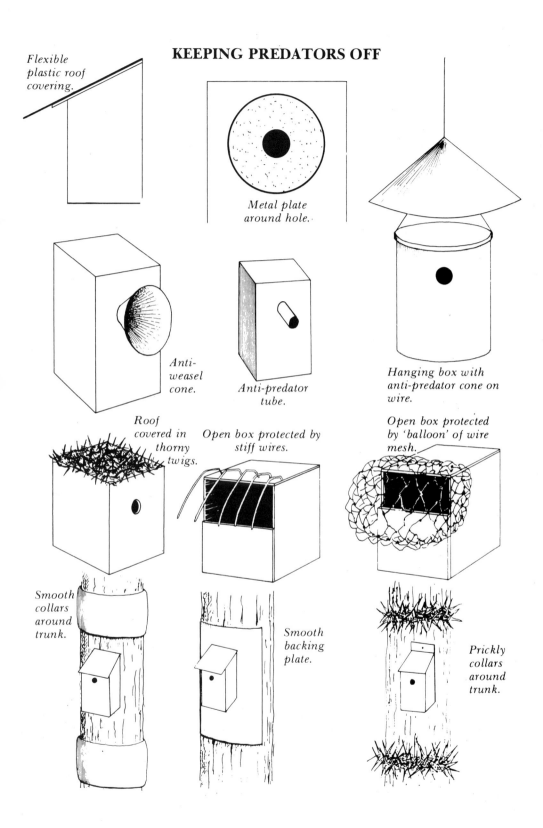

Flexible plastic roof covering.

Metal plate around hole.

Anti-weasel cone.

Anti-predator tube.

Hanging box with anti-predator cone on wire.

Roof covered in thorny twigs.

Open box protected by stiff wires.

Open box protected by 'balloon' of wire mesh.

Smooth collars around trunk.

Smooth backing plate.

Prickly collars around trunk.

predators including cats, Jays, Magpies, Tawny Owls and grey squirrels sit on nestboxes presumably inspecting them for potential food items. Steeply sloping roofs deter this to some extent. Lids must be securely fastened.

Some mammals including weasels and squirrels are deterred by smell, but birds seem not to be. Anti cat and dog pellets (brand name 'Scent-Off' manufactured by Synchemicals Ltd.) obtainable from garden centres can be pushed into the bark below the box. Fresh creosote may help to deter mammals, even a brushful applied on the roof in February may last the season. Local gardening folklore may contain useful ideas, so why not try them? (Fresh orange peel keeps off cats, so one story goes. Does anyone know of any that work?)

Grey squirrels can eat through the wood of the box to gain entry, usually attacking the entrance hole at first and enlarging it. If wood for manufacturing is of varying thickness, use thicker harder wood for the side with the entrance hole. Reinforce holes with chicken wire or metal plates with a large hole but paint them the same colour as the nestbox to make them less conspicuous.

Some birds are predators of nestboxes, Great Spotted Woodpeckers are the most serious. They break into boxes to take the young, often but not always, making the hole low down in the box at the level of the nest cup. Woodpecker damage is worst in years when natural invertebrate food is in short supply. In such years nestling woodpeckers are hungrier and other nestlings noisier and easier to find. Unfortunately, once a woodpecker has discovered nestboxes as a food source it may continue to attack them in another year. Some workers have covered boxes in rubber sheeting. This is too springy for the woodpeckers to hammer through. Again a deep box prevents woodpeckers taking young at the entrance as they jump up hoping for food. Crows and Jays and sometimes Little and Tawny Owls will take the contents of open fronted boxes. The only protection is a balloon of wire about 200mm radius around the front of the box. 40mm chicken wire should work, as will a grill of stiff wire. Weasels, being very slender, will get through these defences.

Humans can be serious predators. As with other species their attentions are often systematic, whether the aim is casual vandalism or serious egg stealing. Measures which make boxes more predator proof can make them more visible to humans. The best defence is well concealed boxes. High in trees hidden by leaves or low in the scrub layer are often good places to conceal boxes, rather than at the traditional 3m on the bare tree trunk. In some extensive schemes nestboxes have been numbered at random to confuse humans wishing to interfere.

If predation is a serious and insoluble problem it is regretfully better to abandon attempts in the area rather than to continue to attract birds to unsafe sites. Rather concentrate on other species or habitats. This applies particularly to endangered, persecuted and open-nesting species.

# PARASITES

Bird nests usually contain other forms of animal life, mostly invertebrates. These include several which have little affect on the birds, but are there only because the box provides a suitable niche for them. Such creatures include earwigs (Dermaptera), tree slugs (*Limax marginatus*) and various moths (Lepidoptera). Sometimes they occur in such great numbers that they must be an irritant to the birds, but for the most part they are of little consequence to them. Next are the predatory creatures like rove beetles (Staphylinidae) and spiders (Araneae) which prey on other invertebrates. There are also scavenging animals like woodlice (Isopoda) and sexton beetles (Silphidae). Finally there are the bird parasites.

The major parasites are fleas (Siphonaptera). These are widespread and can occur in great numbers. Nothing can be done during the breeding season but soon afterwards boxes should be cleaned and the contents thrown some distance away. The action of ejecting the material forces

# MAMMAL BOXES

**Bat box** — *for summer roosting.*

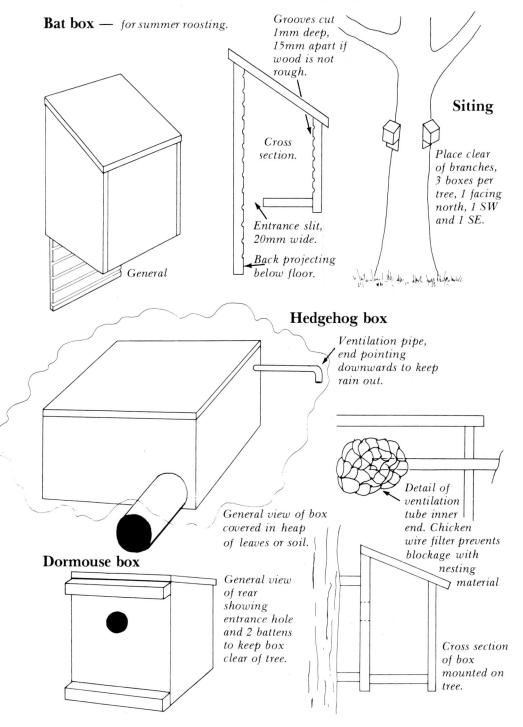

*Grooves cut 1mm deep, 15mm apart if wood is not rough.*

*Cross section.*

*Entrance slit, 20mm wide.*

*Back projecting below floor.*

*General*

### Siting

*Place clear of branches, 3 boxes per tree, 1 facing north, 1 SW and 1 SE.*

## Hedgehog box

*Ventilation pipe, end pointing downwards to keep rain out.*

*General view of box covered in heap of leaves or soil.*

*Detail of ventilation tube inner end. Chicken wire filter prevents blockage with nesting material*

*Cross section of box mounted on tree.*

## Dormouse box

*General view of rear showing entrance hole and 2 battens to keep box clear of tree.*

premature hatching of fleas, and scattering contents at some distance helps to prevent them from returning to the box. This also reduces their chance of survival. Nests should be cleaned with care for the contents may carry human respiratory diseases, often from the white fungal pustules in the damp nest material. Swift and martin nests contain high infestations of flat-flies (Hippoboscidae). For boxes in houses, use a vacuum cleaner for the autumn clean out.

# OTHER USERS

Some animals use nestboxes to the exclusion of birds. They may not evict the birds, but more often occupy the boxes first.

### Invertebrates

Wasps (Vespidae) and some solitary bumble bees (Bombidae) use boxes. There seems to be little reason to destroy either unless they are a nuisance in other ways. Wasps spend most of their year destroying small insect garden pests, and at least a box colony is a known and controllable factor. Wasps use empty boxes, filling them with their spectacular papery nest. Bees nest in the lining of a bird's nest, fluffing it up into a dome shape. Bees may evict the birds but again there is little point in evicting the bees. They will only nest elsewhere, possibly destroying yet another bird nest. Schwegler produce nesting boxes for a variety of insects including ground nesting bees and earwigs. Several species of moth may roost in boxes in large numbers, sometimes for a week or two and occasionally for much longer. Bronze and copper underwing moths (Noctuidae) are perhaps the most spectacular regular inhabitants. Unfortunately birdwatchers seem not to be very good at identifying such invertebrates, many of which provide valuable records for local wildlife trusts and national species distribution recording schemes.

### Mammals

Apart from the predators already mentioned, mice, voles, hedgehogs and bats have used boxes. The fact that mammals use bird nestboxes indicates a lack of natural sites for them too. The solution is to put up purpose-built mammal boxes. Designs are given (page 63) for bats, dormice and hedgehog. Boxes made specifically for mammals should not be treated with preservative; these put off some mammals and worse, may poison others.

As a group, bats are more endangered than are birds. They are protected at all times under the Wildlife and Countryside Act in a similar way to Schedule 1 birds and it is an offence to examine roosting bats without a government licence. A design for a bat summer roost box is illustrated (page 63) but there are plenty of variations possible on the same theme. Bats use different sites at different times of the year, some for hibernating and others for summer roosting or breeding. They do not build any nest in boxes but roost by clinging to the inside timber. For this reason the interior of the box must be of rough wood or have horizontal grooves cut around the inside walls. The bats enter from below through a slit about 20mm wide across the back of the floor. Bat boxes should be about 100mm from back to front. Deeper boxes will not keep the bats close enough together for warmth. The box should be between 100mm and 300mm high, and between 100mm and 150mm wide. Boxes must be draught and rain proof. Site boxes as high as possible in trees or on buildings. There should be no obstructions to flight (e.g. branches or telephone lines) for at least 3m in front of, below, or to the sides of the box, and none for 1m above the box. Before attempting any major work with bat boxes read 'Bat Boxes' published by FFPS. For those who dislike bats inside the house, why not put bat boxes on the outside of the house just underneath the eaves?

Hedgehogs use Tunnel and Chamber type boxes. The chamber is a cube, the length of each side being about 300mm, and its entrance tunnel is 200mm long and 100mm in diameter or cross section. Some people have enjoyed instant success with these boxes whilst (as for birds) others wait in vain. The box should be sited on the ground underneath a heap of leaves or soil with only the entrance and ventilation tube protruding. There must be an adequate supply of dead leaves near the box for nesting material. Ensure the ventilation tube cannot become clogged with leaves by putting a wire mesh filter over the inner end.

Dormice, both common and edible, use boxes. Common dormice (*Muscardinus avellanarius*) are protected and should not be trapped, killed or disturbed. Edible dormice (*Glis glis*) have been introduced in the Chilterns from Europe. Any small box will do but it is more convenient for them to have an entrance hole adjacent to the tree trunk for ease of access. One design (page 63) has the entrance between the box and trunk, the box held about 30mm away from the trunk by wooden spacers. The same design has been used occasionally by Treecreepers.

Some other species of mouse and vole use occupied bird boxes. Wood mice (*Sylvaemus sylvaticus*), yellow-necked mice (*Sylvaemus flavicollis*) and bank voles (*Clethrionomys glareolus*) are particularly good tree climbers. There is little point in destroying their nests as they are not large-scale nest predators and do form part of owl diets. You can provide suitable shelter sites for small mammals simply by leaving a covered area of soft earth. Slates or tiles etc. supported on stones will do for mice and voles to live under. They will also take to tunnel nestboxes. These should be about 150mm long with a 100mm cross section and a 25mm entrance hole at one end. Insert the box in a bank or heap of earth.

It is of little use providing boxes for mammals unless the habitat is suitable. Hedgehogs, for instance, will be unlikely to use a box in a garden which has no wild patches, no compost heap, no shelter and is frequently dosed with pesticides.

There are several booklets mentioned in the Appendix which give much more detailed information about boxes for other users.

# INSPECTION AND RECORDING

**The BTO Nest Record Scheme**

Nestboxes provide ideal tools for studying breeding birds - natural sites can often be difficult to locate, inspect and record reliably. Nests in boxes are easier to manipulate for experimental purposes. The BTO Nest Record Scheme handles information recorded from nestboxes (as well as that from natural sites). This information, which is now stored on computer files, can be analysed to show anything from basic breeding biology of a species to annual, regional or habitat-related variations in breeding performance for common species.

The Nest Record Scheme is just one of several BTO surveys. Others include censusing breeding populations of birds in woodland, farmland and waterways; counting wading birds on estuaries in winter; counting birds feeding in gardens and ringing birds. Each year there are short term surveys of particular species or groups. Results from some of these surveys, including those from the Nest Record Scheme are being combined in the BTO's Integrated Population Monitoring programme (IPM). This programme is of great importance to conservation. It can detect declines in bird populations at an early stage, give some understanding of the causes of declines and therefore highlight steps which may be taken to reverse them. The IPM provides the best possible nation-wide monitoring scheme for our common and not-so-common birds. It is only the combined efforts of our enthusiastic volunteer birdwatchers that allows the BTO to assess the 'health' of our bird populations each year in order that conservation bodies may have the best possible information on which to base their work.

By recording events, even only in the odd garden nestbox, it is possible to help in this national effort for conservation. It doesn't matter if a nest ends in failure - the scheme needs information on failure as much as on success. The Nest Record Cards (page 67) are available free from BTO together with an explanatory booklet (see Appendix for address).

The most important items to be recorded are listed below and visits to a nest should be timed if possible with these in mind.

1. Building. Best observed from a distance.
2. Afternoon visits to find date of first egg. Eggs are normally laid in the morning, so a new egg found in the afternoon will be most likely to be an egg of that day.
3. During incubation, one early visit to record the number of eggs laid and another nearer hatching to record whether the eggs are still present and being incubated.
4. Two or three days after hatching to record the number of eggs hatched.
5. Two-thirds through the nestling period to record the number of nestlings which survived through the hatching process.
6. Fledging date. Best observed from a distance. Close inspection at this time may force a premature departure.
7. After fledging. Record the number of unhatched eggs and dead young remaining: some may have been removed by parent birds.
8. Check about weekly for signs of a second clutch.

**Inspecting Nests**

**Under the Wildlife and Countryside Act (1981) it is an offence to disturb or even approach a Schedule 1 bird at the nest, or to handle any wild bird without a licence. Licences for various operations can be obtained by suitably qualified people from the BTO.** The Appendix gives some more details of these.

Whenever inspecting nests of any sort, the welfare of the birds must be placed before other

# NEST RECORD CARD

*Front*

**Species:** STARLING  
**County/Region:** GBNT  
**19 9 2** Year  BTO Ref.

**Observer** | **Code:** C D F  
**Locality (Place-Name):** BECKINGHAM  
**Grid Ref.:** S K 7 7 8 9 0 3

**Altitude:** 15 m  
**Male Parent Age:** Ring No.:  
**Female Parent Age:** Ring No.:  *(For Ringer's Use Only)*

| Day | Mth. | Hour | Number of Eggs | Yng. | Status Codes (A two-letter code per column see coding card) | | COMMENTS (Include Behaviour, Ringing, Measurements etc.) |
|---|---|---|---|---|---|---|---|
| 14 | 04 | 16 | 0 | | N4 | | |
| 22 | 04 | 16 | 5 | | WA | AN | |
| 25 | 04 | 12 | 5 | | WA | AN | |
| 03 | 05 | 08 | | 5 | TO | BL | |
| 09 | 05 | 09 | | 5 | IP | YR | |
| 16 | 05 | 11 | | 5 | FM | AF | |
| 23 | 05 | 11 | | 5 | SL | | |
| 30 | 05 | 08 | | | MR | | RJ36559 retrapped in garden |

**Ring Numbers of Young**  
First Number in Series: RJ36556  
Last Number in Series: RJ36560

100150/B2603921/5203

PLEASE RETURN TO BTO, NATIONAL CENTRE FOR ORNITHOLOGY, THE NUNNERY, THETFORD, NORFOLK IP24 2PU  
PLEASE MAKE NO GUESSES (PLEASE RECORD FURTHER VISITS ON AN EXTRA CARD STAPLED TO THIS ONE)  
British Trust for Ornithology

*Back*

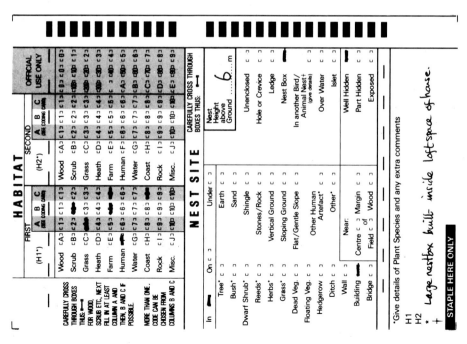

**HABITAT**

FIRST (H1*): Wood, Scrub, Grass, Heath, Farm, Human, Water, Coast, Rock, Misc. — columns A B C

SECOND (H2*): Wood, Scrub, Grass, Heath, Farm, Human, Water, Coast, Rock, Misc. — columns A B C

CAREFULLY CROSS THROUGH BOXES THUS → ■

FOR WOOD, SCRUB ETC, NEXT FILL IN AT LEAST COLUMN A AND THEN, B AND C IF POSSIBLE

MORE THAN ONE. CODE CAN BE CHOSEN FROM COLUMNS B AND C

**NEST SITE**

Nest Height above Ground: 6 m

In / On / Under

Tree*, Bush*, Dwarf Shrub*, Reeds*, Herbs*, Grass*, Dead Veg., Floating Veg., Hedgerow, Ditch, Wall, Building, Bridge

Unenclosed, Hole or Crevice, Ledge, Nest Box, In another Bird/Animal Nest† (give details), Over Water, Islet, Well Hidden, Part Hidden, Exposed

Near: Centre / Margin, Field / Wood, Other Human Artefact*, Other*

*Give details of Plant Species and any extra comments  
H1  
H2  
* + Large nestbox built inside loftspace of house.

STAPLE HERE ONLY

67

considerations. Fortunately most species are fairly tolerant of a sensitive human approach, although a few individuals do object. Since most birds have little or no sense of smell, there is no need to fear that they will smell that a human has interfered with the nest in their absence. Mammalian predators do have a keen sense of smell and can follow tracks made by us, so take care not to lead them to a ready food source. Visits may be made as often as once a day with very tolerant birds, but this is not necessary except in some very detailed studies.

In some cases it is better if a sitting bird is gently encouraged to leave its nestbox before it is opened. A human face appearing as the roof opens must be a worrying sight! Tap the tree trunk or nestbox gently and the bird will probably leave. Some individuals will sit tight under all circumstances. It is best not to disturb these - visit the box when the tight sitter is away feeding. In general, as the nest progresses, birds become less likely to desert as a result of disturbance because investment in the young is greater. Egg laying and hatching times can be particularly sensitive. Some species are liable to desert if handled at the nest, and these are mentioned in 'Species Notes'.

When counting eggs in the nest, take care to find all the eggs, which may be very well hidden deep in the nest material. With eggs of small birds exercise extreme care when hunting for hidden ones - the shells are very thin. Inspecting late in the nest cycle must be done with great care. Adults are most tolerant at this time, but the young are liable to fledge prematurely if disturbed. This is an adaptation to counter predator attacks. With hole entrance boxes, if the young explode in this way, gather them up and post them back through the entrance hole. Put your hand over the hole for a few minutes whilst the young settle, then quietly move away.

When inspecting boxes closely, care should be taken to avoid inhaling any dust or other matter from old nests. Boxes may contain, among other things, white pustules of a keratin-eating fungus. (Keratin is the material of which feathers are made.) This fungus can grow in the warm damp human lung and is not easy to remove. It is also easy to catch various intestinal disorders from nest contents. Always wash your hands after dealing with nests and before eating your sandwiches!

Contributors to the Nest Record Scheme should note that, in general, records from open nests that have had anti-predator devices placed around them are not desirable. The number of nests protected in this way is minute compared to the total number of all nests, yet this tiny number could provide the bulk of the recorded nests. Such a situation would cause severe bias in the Nest Record data. Boxes which have been protected from predators before being selected by birds are in a different category and should be recorded. The nature of the protection should be indicated clearly on the card. If in doubt in a particular situation, consult the Nest Record Officer at the BTO.

**Nestbox Studies**

Recording the basic information on each nest is only the starting point of nestbox studies. The fact that boxes are built, and therefore not natural, allows inclusion of devices to aid observation and recording. For example, glass-backed boxes can be made and fixed on the side of a hide or against a window. Observations can be made from the darkened room behind the window.

Detailed studies which require knowledge of the identities of the adult birds may require trapping at the nest. Ringers will be familiar with the mandatory instructions for trapping birds at nestboxes. These, briefly, state that in all cases where birds are trapped at nestboxes the boxes should be numbered and recorded on a map, a written note must be made each time a trap is set at a nestbox and that there must be a fail-safe procedure ensuring that nest entrances which have been blocked are unblocked.

Non-ringers are not subject to the letter of these guidelines, and in any case will not be trapping or handling birds at the nest (which requires a general ringing permit together with an endorsement for nest trapping). However it is possible that non-ringers may wish to block entrance holes from time to time, to prevent birds flying out in alarm for instance. These guidelines should be adhered to. All boxes with hole entrances which may be blocked temporarily during inspection must be numbered and recorded on a map. The map should be available in the field. Holes should only be blocked with a cloth specifically for that purpose and each person should carry at most one such cloth. Before and after a nestbox checking session, all cloths must be checked. A record of boxes inspected must be made as each box is inspected. Perhaps the simplest and safest method to adopt is to tie the cloth to your ladder or to your clothing with a short string. It is then impossible to leave the cloth in the box as you depart.

Various automatic recording devices have been used. These include cameras triggered by the entry of a bird or by a clock. Micro- or light-sensitive switches attached at the entrance can be used to record frequency of parental visits. It is quite easy to attach recording devices to a microcomputer. This has the advantages that data collected will be held on computer file ready for analysis and that computer collection is more flexible than other automatic methods. It is important to be aware that automatic data collection will provide a very detailed picture of events at the nestbox being monitored. There is the danger that the nest being monitored is atypical. It is wise to monitor several nests in depth before drawing conclusions about the whole species. The BBC microcomputer is probably the most suitable machine for automatic data collection. It is, admittedly, old but because of this it is easy to find a very cheap second-hand machine. Further, the BBC includes two input ports (the user port and analogue port) which were designed with this sort of operation in mind. More modern computers may only include such ports as extras and in any case are often too heavily used to be spared for a long-term data collection operation. There are also some remote battery-powered data collection devices available (such as EMU and VELA). These may be left collecting data in the field far away from electric power supplies. Once data have been collected they may be transferred to a computer for analysis. There are a range of devices available for recording humidity, light, oxygen, pH, movement and temperature. Costs range from a pound or two for home-made sensing devices to several hundreds of pounds for top-of-the-range equipment. The Appendix gives details of some equipment suppliers.

Nestbox populations of birds like the commoner tits can be studied in order to throw light on a large number of general biological problems. These include mate choice, mate fidelity, nest site fidelity in male or female, brood parasitism (not only with Cuckoos, also Starling and probably many others) and reproductive success. Coupled with wider bird ringing work, data from ringing nestlings is important for investigations into juvenile and adult survival and juvenile dispersal. Remains of birds including rings are often found in owl and raptor nests. Searching for them may not always be pleasant but it is always worthwhile. Owl pellets and nestbox debris also allow studies of owl diets. Boxes may also be inspected by night for roosting birds (provided the appropriate ringing permits are held). This operation should not be carried out more often than once every three or four weeks and should not be carried out in very cold weather.

There are numerous other fields of study in which nestboxes can be used. There has been very little basic recording of nestbox invertebrate fauna. Contacts with entomologists will help for identification purposes. Identification of box contents is quite likely to provide new records of species simply because of the present under-recorded state. Basic recording can be followed by ecological studies. Even a garden tit nestbox can provide 12 months continuous entomological observation!

## Record Keeping

In any nestbox project, details of all boxes should be kept systematically. Boxes must be labelled. The simplest method is to use a spirit-based marking pen (Berol Toughpoint marker pens are very good). Numbering the box takes only a few seconds and the mark lasts several seasons. This is much cleaner and easier than painting numbers. Maps of box locations are essential if more than a handful of boxes are put up or if a detailed recording scheme is operated. The details recorded about boxes will vary according to the nature of the scheme but will probably include box location, type and size, habitat, height, aspect and site.

Maps are essential. It may appear to you, as you site your boxes in the autumn or winter when there is little undergrowth, that it will be easy to find them again. Experience shows that boxes can easily become hard to find as the rampant spring and summer undergrowth develops. Memory does not always work, even between one weekly visit and another, particularly when you are tired after a long field session. Even within the space of a week or two the development of undergrowth can hide a box completely.

## Recording Technique

People vary in the way they deal with information. It is impossible to state the 'best' way to record events in nestboxes. The ideas below are some which have been found to be useful. Your own system may develop differently but no one dealing with nestboxes should be without a reliable and efficient recording system. Your system should allow you know what to expect when you are visiting each box - recording errors can be detected and unusual observations can be double checked on the spot.

Small hardbacked note books can be used. They require that details of boxes to be visited, together with notes about what to look for, be written before a field visit is made. Other people have found that small ring binders or filofaxes are more useful. These will have one page to each nest and the pages arranged in the order of visiting nests. This has the advantage that the complete nest history is available to you at the nestbox. Inconsistent or unlikely observations can be double-checked on the spot. This enables more reliable data recording. Ring binders can also hold the other vital bits of paper and card - like your maps and the sheet of codes used by the Nest Record Scheme. Records should be transcribed into a permanent format (e.g. nest record cards) as soon as possible, record cards being updated visit by visit. Modern reprographic and desk-top publishing equipment, now widely available, is very useful for producing field sheets of exactly the format desired.

With large numbers of boxes it may be helpful to plot a calendar of events on large sheets of graph paper. This will show when boxes need visiting and when they should be left unvisited. Ordinary graph paper will do, but a wide range of specialist graph papers, including some calendar type of graphs, is available from stationers. 'Chartwell' produce a wide range of high quality graph papers. Another method of helping to plan visits is to record the information on a computer spreadsheet. These can calculate important dates, such as projected hatching or fledging dates, using the data already entered (first egg date and number of eggs).

In the field, always record information on the spot. Do not commit anything to memory even for only a few seconds. A minor crisis or distraction can easily cause the transposition of numbers - 6 eggs in box 45 becoming 5 in 46. The illustrations of notes from a field book, nest record card etc. are intended as an example of what have been found useful. Some observers use a hand-held cassette recorder for recording events, others use an automatic camera for a permanent record of nests particularly those high in trees.

Be prepared for all sorts of events before you start field work. With experience you will know what equipment you may need, but rather than committing it to memory write a check list in the back of the field book. If you are visiting an area seldom visited by other people, make sure someone knows where you will be. Ensure you have all the equipment before you set off.

Your check list may include:
*pen - which works in the wet,*
*pencil (for when you lose the pen),*
*note book (and a spare for when the first becomes soaked),*
*torch and dentist's mirror for looking into Wren and other nests,*
*hammer,*
*nails,*
*string,*
*metal hole reinforcements,*
*knife,*
*mirror on a long stick for looking into high open nests,*
*ladder,*
*first aid kit with insect repellent,*
*anti-mammal pellets,*
*cloth for blocking holes,*
*Nest Record Scheme coding sheet,*
*map of nestboxes.*

## Extract from Notebook with explanatory notes.

The two-letter 'activity codes', WA, AN, BL, etc. are from the BTO Nest Record coding system. This is fully described in the booklet 'The Nest Record Scheme', free to participants in the scheme from the BTO at Thetford.

| Page from field book | Explanation |
|---|---|
| 25/04/92  12.00-13.00 | |
| | |
| 1  Starling  5E  WA  AN | 5 warm eggs; adult at the nest. |
| 7  Blue Tit  7Y  BL | 7 young birds; still blind. |
| 4  Starling  5Y  IP  AV | 5 young; primary feathers in pin; adult near nest. |
| 5  Starling  6Y  IP  AV | 6 young; otherwise as box 4. |
| 6  Great Tit 8E  WA  UN | 8 eggs; warm and not covered with lining. |
| 9  Starling  5Y  BL  AV | 5 young; still blind, adult nearby. |

# APPENDIX

**1        Useful Addresses**

| | |
|---|---|
| **British Trust for Ornithology** | **BTO, The National Centre for Ornithology, The Nunnery, Thetford, Norfolk, IP24 2PU** |
| Bat Conservation Trust | BCT, The London Ecology Centre, Shelton St., Covent Garden, London. |
| British Hedgehog Preservation Society | BHPS, Knowbury House, Ludlow, Shropshire, SY8 3LQ |
| Countryside Council for Wales | CCW, Hafod Elfyn, Ffordd Penrhos, Penrhos Road, Bangor, Gwynedd, LL57 2LQ |
| Department of the Environment for Northern Ireland, Calvert House, 23 Castle Place, Belfast, BT1 1FY | |
| English Nature | EN, Northminster House, Peterborough, PE1 1UA |
| Fauna and Flora Preservation Society | FFPS, 1 Kensington Gore, London, SW7 2AR |
| The Hawk and Owl Trust | Director C. Shawyer, c/o Zoological Society of London, Regent's Park, London, NW1 4RY |
| Henry Doubleday Research Association | HDRA, Ryton Organic Gardens, Ryton-on-Dunsmore, Coventry, CV8 3LG |
| Mammal Society | Dept of Zoology, Bristol University, Woodland Road, Bristol, BS8 1UG |
| Royal Society for Nature Conservation | RSNC, The Green, Witham Park, Lincoln, LN5 7JR |
| Royal Society for the Protection of Birds | RSPB, The Lodge, Sandy, Beds., SG19 2DL |
| Scottish Natural Heritage | SNH, 2-5, Anderson Place, Edinburgh, EH6 5NP |

**2        Who to Contact**

| | |
|---|---|
| Bird Surveys, (Nest Records scheme and others) | BTO |
| Licences for Schedule 1 birds (ringing or recording at nest) | BTO |
| Licences for Schedule 1 birds (photography at nest etc.) | EN, CCW or SNH |
| Hedgehog Box plans | HDRA or BHPS |
| Birds and the Law | RSPB |

**3        Further Reading and Information**

The New Atlas of Breeding Birds of Britain and Ireland: 1988-1991; Gibbons, Reid & Chapman. (1993, T & AD Poyser, London)
> The breeding distribution, numbers and habitats used by Britain and Ireland's birds.

The Audubon Society Guide to Attracting Birds; Kress (1985, Scribner's, New York)
> The American garden bird book with sections on preventing parasites and predators.

Bat Boxes; Stebbings and Walsh (1988, FFPS)
> Designs and other information about bats.

Bats in Houses; Hutson (1990, FFPS)
> Booklet about all aspects of conservation of bats for the householder.

Birds of the Western Palaearctic Vols 1-8; Cramp et al (1977-1994, Oxford)
> The most up-to-date and comprehensive book available for information on all aspects of bird life.

Britain's Birds in 1990-91: Stroud and Glue (1992, BTO/JNCC)
> The second annual report of the status of birds in Britain compiled from various major surveys and projects.

Collins Guide to Wildlife about the House and Home; Mourier, Winding & Sunesen (1977, Collins)
> Contains information on various other nestbox inhabitants.

Directory of Grant Making Trusts, 12th Compilation; (1991, Charities Aid Foundation)
> Contains information on grants from various charities.

A Field Guide to Nests, Eggs and Nestlings of British and European Birds; Harrison (1975, Collins)
> Essential for identification of nests and eggs and other background information.

Finding and Identifying Mammals in Britain; Corbett (1975, British Museum)
> For identifying remains in owl pellets and live box users.

The Garden Bird Book; Glue (1982, Macmillan.)
> Information on birds and the garden, including results of some BTO surveys.

A Guide to Little Tern Conservation; Haddon & Knight (1983, RSPB)
> An advanced guide also relevant to other major nest site protection projects.

Hedgehogs in your Garden; Sedgeley (1991, Mammal Society)
> All aspects of hedgehog conservation for the gardener.

The Identification of Remains in Owl Pellets; Yalden (1977, Mammal Society)
> Essential booklet for anyone with more than a passing interest in owl pellets.

Nestboxes for the Birds of Britain and Europe; Bolund (1987, Sainsbury press)
> A translation of a Scandinavian book which has additional background information about some of our rarer species of nestbox birds.

The Nest Record Scheme; BTO
> Free booklet for nest recorders. It contains full details of the scheme and coding system.

The New Bird Table Book; Soper (1986, David & Charles)
> Additional information on garden birds.

Population Trends in British Birds; Marchant, Hudson, Carter and Whittington (1990, BTO/NCC)
> Results of thirty years of BTO populations surveys.

Restoration of Gravel Pits for Wildfowl; Street (1985, Game Conservancy)
> An advanced guide which includes designs and instructions for wildfowl nest boxes.

Rivers and Wildlife Handbook; Lewis and Willows (1984, RSPB/RSNC)
> An advanced guide with several wetland and wildfowl designs.

Wildlife, the Law and You; (1982, NCC)
> A brief guide to the 1981 Wildlife & Countryside Act.


**4          Equipment Suppliers**

The ACO Company, Hitchin Road, Shefford, Bedfordshire, SG17 5JS
> This company produces polymerised concrete built-in nestboxes together with some other built-in wildlife protection equipment.

A & P Chambers, Kaluna House, Nairnside, Inverness, IV1 2BU
> Chambers produce off-the-shelf and made-to-order automatic monitoring systems for use with various computer systems.

C.J. Wildbird Foods, The Rea, Upton Magna, Shrewsbury, SY4 4UB
> Suppliers of a range of nestboxes including House Martin boxes. They also supply a wide range of garden bird products and wild bird food.

The Halo Company, Osborne House, Station Road, Burgess Hill, West Sussex, RH15 9EH

> Halo are developing plastic nestboxes which, it is hoped, overcome the problems normally associated with the material.

Marley Building Materials Ltd., Marketing Dept., Station Road, Coleshill, Birmingham, B46 1HP

> Marley produce roofing tiles with integral Swift nest entrances.

Philip Harris Education, Lynn Lane, Shenstone, Lichfield, WS14 0EE

> Manufacturers of automatic monitoring equipment, some of which can be used in nestboxes.

Redland Roof Tiles, Technical dept., Castle Court, 41, London Road, Reigate, Surrey, RH2 9BY

> Redland produces ridge end roof tile boxes and others to order.

RSPB (Address given in Appendix 1).

> Their catalogue contains items of interest including small nestboxes and (in the spring catalogue) House Martin nests.

Schwegler-Vogelschutzgeräte GmbH, Heinkelstraße 35, 7060, Schorndorf, Germany.

> This company produces a wide variety of nestboxes for birds and other animals. Their catalogue alone is worth looking at for its ideas including anti-predator devices. A few garden centres stock their sawdust/cement nestboxes.

University of Hull, D Ainley, Department of Educational Studies, Cottingham Road, Hull, HU6 7RX

> The department produces low-cost monitoring hardware and software for use with the BBC microcomputer, initially developed for use in schools.

## 5 Acknowledgements

This guide is the result of many years' accumulated experience of amateur and professional ornithologists. Without their willingness to give of their time and experience this guide would not be possible. On behalf of the birds who will benefit from better provision of nest sites I thank them all. In addition to those who have been acknowledged in earlier editions the following people, BTO staff and others, have made new contributions to this edition.

| K Baker | P Beaven | B Brown | D Bryant | M Canham |
| E Cowley | H Crick | A Davies | A de Potier | A del Novo |
| J Dodd | A Fox | D Garner | D Glue | A Gosler |
| L Y Green | P Green | J G Greenwood | J J D Greenwood | G Grine |
| A Haigh | P Harrison | A Heaton | P Johnson | B Little |
| C Lowe | C Mead | D Norman | V Pickup | H Robb |
| S Tyler | R Smith | H Williams | S Wright | |

As with earlier editions it is not intended that this is to be the last word on nestboxes - the files remain open. The BTO Nest Record Officer will be pleased to accept suggestions, comments or contributions at any time,

## 6 Cutting Diagrams

The following pages give cutting diagrams for nestboxes to be made from planks or sheets of wood. It must be stressed that the exact dimensions are not critical in general, and it is better to make the box,according to the wood rather than to waste expensive wood.

# Cutting diagrams for small boxes

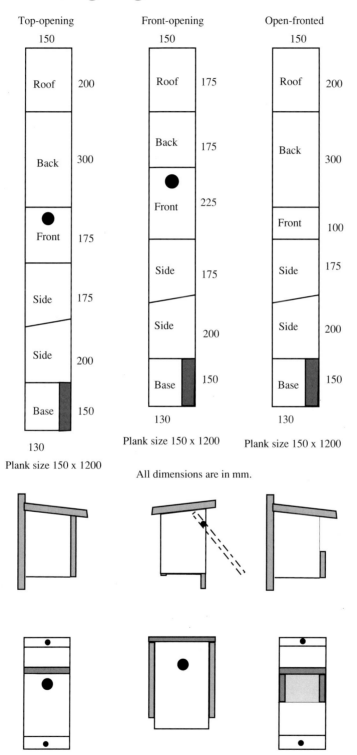

Top-opening

150

| Roof | 200 |
| Back | 300 |
| Front | 175 |
| Side | 175 |
| Side | 200 |
| Base | 150 |

130

Plank size 150 x 1200

Front-opening

150

| Roof | 175 |
| Back | 175 |
| Front | 225 |
| Side | 175 |
| Side | 200 |
| Base | 150 |

130

Plank size 150 x 1200

Open-fronted

150

| Roof | 200 |
| Back | 300 |
| Front | 100 |
| Side | 175 |
| Side | 200 |
| Base | 150 |

130

Plank size 150 x 1200

All dimensions are in mm.

# Plan for a pole-mounted Barn Owl box

## Cutting Diagram

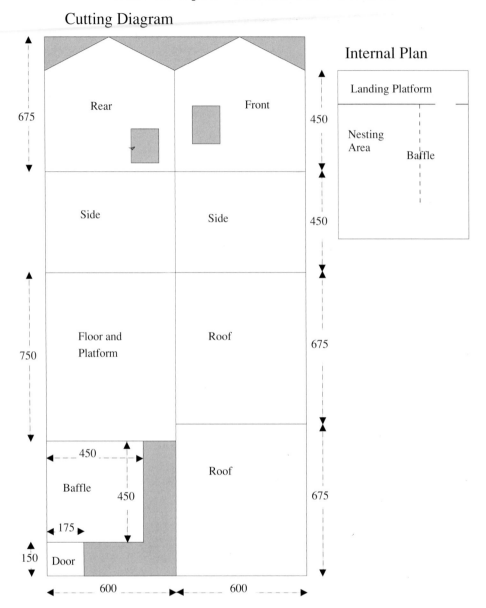

This box needs one 8'x4' sheet of ¾" exterior ply. The rear panel has a 125mm by 150mm inspection hatch near the bottom corner with a door cut slightly larger. The interior baffle screening the nest chamber does not reach up to the roof - the space above it aids ventilation.

The landing area and exercise platform in front of the entrance is vital for boxes situated in exposed or treeless areas.

This is a large and heavy box. Erecting it requires care and planning in order to ensure the box will withstand winter gales.

# 7       Species Index

Species referred to are listed here in alphabetical order of English name. Page references in bold are main entries in Species Notes. Also included are Schedule 1 species which may use artificial nest sites but are not referred to elsewhere in the book. Schedule 1 species are indicated. A full list of Schedule 1 birds is available form the BTO or RSPB. The column NRC shows the approximate number of Nest Record Cards submitted each year together with up to two letters. I means that nest records are already used by the BTO Integrated Population Monitoring programme; M shows that more cards for the species are particularly required. More species are being added to the IPM programme each year as back data are stored on computer files - some tits are to be included next.

| English Name | Scientific Name | Page | Schedule 1 | NRC | |
|---|---|---|---|---|---|
| Barn Owl | Tyto alba | **48** | Schedule 1 | 200 | I |
| Black Guillemot (Tystie) | Cepphus grylle | **46** | | 40 | |
| Black-necked Grebe | Podiceps nigricollis | | Schedule 1 | 1 | |
| Black Redstart | Phoenicurus ochruros | **55** | Schedule 1 | 5 | |
| Black-tailed Godwit | Limosa limosa | 45 | Schedule 1 | 1 | |
| Black-throated Diver | Gavia arctica | 41 | Schedule 1 | 5 | |
| Blackbird | Turdus merula | 55 | | 2000 | |
| Blue Tit | Parus caeruleus | **57** | | 3000 | |
| Canada Goose | Branta canadensis | 42 | | 200 | |
| Crow | Corvus corone | 50 | | 200 | I |
| Chaffinch | Fringilla coelebs | 40 | | 400 | I |
| Coal Tit | Parus ater | **57** | | 100 | |
| Common Tern | Sterna hirundo | **46** | | 200 | |
| Coot | Fulica atra | 45 | | 500 | |
| Crested Tit | Parus cristatus | **57** | Schedule 1 | 10 | |
| Cuckoo | Cuculus canorus | 69 | | 20 | |
| Dipper | Cinclus cinclus | **54** | | 300 | |
| Feral Pigeon | Columba livia | **47** | | 100 | |
| Goldeneye | Bucephala clangula | **43** | | 5 | |
| Goldfinch | Carduelis carduelis | 40 | | 60 | |
| Goosander | Mergus merganser | **44** | | 10 | |
| Goshawk | Accipiter gentilis | 44 | Schedule 1 | 30 | |
| Great Crested Grebe | Podiceps cristatus | **42** | | 100 | |
| Great Northern Diver | Gavia immer | 41 | Schedule 1 | 0 | |
| Great Spotted Woodpecker | Dendrocopos major | **52** | | 10 | |
| Great Tit | Parus major | **57** | | 2000 | |
| Green Woodpecker | Picus viridis | **52** | | 10 | |
| Greenshank | Tringa nebularia | 45 | Schedule 1 | 1 | |
| Grey Wagtail | Motacilla cinerea | **53** | | 200 | IM |
| Greylag Goose | Anser anser | | Schedule 1 | 10 | |
| Hobby | Falco subbuteo | 44 | Schedule 1 | 20 | |
| Hoopoe | Upupa epops | 41 | Schedule 1 | 0 | |
| House Martin | Delichon urbica | **53** | | 500 | |
| House Sparrow | Passer domesticus | **59** | | 200 | |
| Jackdaw | Corvus monedula | **58** | | 300 | |
| Jay | Garrulus glandarius | 41 | | 40 | |
| Kestrel | Falco tinnunculus | **44** | | 200 | I |
| Kingfisher | Alcedo atthis | **51** | Schedule 1 | 30 | |
| Kittiwake | Rissa tridactyla | **45** | | 200 | |
| Lapwing | Vanellus vanellus | 45 | | 500 | I |

| | | | | | |
|---|---|---|---|---|---|
| Lesser Spotted Woodpecker | *Dendrocopos minor* | **52** | | 6 | |
| Little Owl | *Athene noctua* | **49** | | 40 | |
| Little Ringed Plover | *Charadrius dubius* | 45 | Schedule 1 | 50 | |
| Little Tern | *Sterna albifrons* | **46** | Schedule 1 | 200 | |
| Long-eared Owl | *Asio otus* | **50** | | 30 | |
| Mallard | *Anas platyrhynchos* | 43 | | 200 | |
| Magpie | *Pica pica* | 60 | | 300 | I |
| Mandarin | *Aix galericulata* | **43** | | 10 | |
| Manx Shearwater | *Puffinus puffinus* | 42 | | 2 | |
| Marsh Tit | *Parus palustris* | **56** | | 30 | |
| Meadow Pipit | *Anthus pratensis* | 52 | | 200 | IM |
| Merlin | *Falco columbarius* | **44** | Schedule 1 | 200 | IM |
| Moorhen | *Gallinula chloropus* | 45 | | 400 | I |
| Mute Swan | *Cygnus olor* | 42 | | 300 | IM |
| Nightjar | *Caprimulgus europaeus* | **50** | | 100 | IM |
| Nuthatch | *Sitta europaea* | **58** | | 200 | I |
| Osprey | *Pandion haliaetus* | 44 | Schedule 1 | 2 | |
| Peregrine | *Falco peregrinus* | 45 | Schedule 1 | 100 | IM |
| Pied Flycatcher | *Ficedula hypoleuca* | **56** | | 2000 | |
| Pied Wagtail | *Motacilla alba* | **54** | | 300 | I |
| Puffin | *Fratercula arctica* | 42 | | 10 | |
| Red-breasted Merganser | *Mergus serrator* | **43** | | 2 | |
| Red Kite | *Milvus milvus* | 44 | Schedule 1 | 1 | |
| Red-throated Diver | *Gavia stellata* | 41 | Schedule 1 | 50 | |
| Redshank | *Tringa totanus* | 45 | | 40 | |
| Redstart | *Phoenicurus phoenicurus* | 55 | | 200 | I |
| Reed Bunting | *Emberiza schoeniclus* | 41 | | 100 | IM |
| Ring-necked Parakeet | *Psittacula krameri* | **47** | | 1 | |
| Robin | *Erithacus rubecula* | 55 | | 400 | IM |
| Roseate Tern | *Sterna dougallii* | **45** | Schedule 1 | 30 | |
| Sand Martin | *Riparia riparia* | **52** | | 20 | |
| Short-toed Treecreeper | *Certhia brachydactyla* | | Schedule 1 | 0 | |
| Shelduck | *Tadorna tadorna* | **42** | | 10 | |
| Skylark | *Alauda arvensis* | 52 | | 100 | IM |
| Slavonian Grebe | *Podiceps auritus* | | Schedule 1 | 4 | |
| Snipe | *Gallinago gallinago* | 45 | | 20 | |
| Song Thrush | *Turdus philomelos* | 55 | | 800 | I |
| Spotted Flycatcher | *Muscicapa striata* | **56** | | 200 | I |
| Starling | *Sturnus vulgaris* | **58** | | 400 | I |
| Stock Dove | *Columba oenas* | **47** | | 200 | I |
| Stone-curlew | *Burhinus oedicnemus* | 45 | Schedule 1 | 5 | |
| Storm Petrel | *Hydrobates pelagicus* | 42 | | 3 | |
| Swallow | *Hirundo rustica* | **53** | | 2000 | I |
| Swift | *Apus apus* | **50** | | 30 | |
| Tawny Owl | *Strix aluco* | **49** | | 300 | I |
| Tree Sparrow | *Passer montanus* | **59** | | 300 | |
| Treecreeper | *Certhia familiaris* | **58** | | 70 | |
| Wheatear | *Oenanthe oenanthe* | 55 | | 90 | IM |
| Willow Tit | *Parus montanus* | **57** | | 10 | |
| Wood Duck | *Aix sponsa* | 41 | | 0 | |
| Wren | *Troglodytes troglodytes* | **54** | | 300 | I |
| Wryneck | *Jynx torquilla* | **51** | Schedule 1 | 1 | |
| Yellow Wagtail | *Motacilla flava* | 52 | | 20 | |

# You've enjoyed the book, now join the BTO!

For amateur birdwatchers, the British Trust for Ornithology (BTO) is Britain's premier bird-research organisation. Our members participate in all kinds of nation–wide investigations into Britain's birds. By combining the observations of thousands of volunteers we gain unique information on Britain's birds. Our investigations deal with all aspects of the lives of our birds and include distribution, habitat preferences, population numbers, migration and, of course, nesting behaviour.

The BTO is very firmly a membership based organisation with almost 10,000 members and a staff of around 60, based in Norfolk, who organise the surveys and collate the information gathered. With much of the work, members of the 130–strong volunteer Regional Network provide the link between the staff and the observer in the field. If you would like to join us, just contact the Membership Secretary by telephoning 0842 750050.

Many of our members take part in one of our very practical schemes for making their own birdwatching activities count. Quite apart from long–term investigations, each year sees the introduction of new, short–term research projects to investigate particular problems. For instance, there are single species surveys – Nightjars were the target in summer 1992 and the results have shown that the population nationally has increased 50% since the last survey in 1981. Detailed work on organic farms started in 1992 and is due to continue into 1994. We have designed the investigation to find out whether organic husbandry is better for birds than conventional management.

Over the last few years we have organised, for members living near the coast, a succession of special investigations, often of particular estuaries. These special surveys supplement the long–running counts of waders on our estuaries.

The BTO publishes *BTO News* six times a year to keep members in touch with national and local events and issues, and there is a programme of national conferences and regional meetings each year. The BTO also publishes a series of Guides (of which this is one) of practical use to birdwatchers, and also two scientific journals, *Bird Study* and *Ringing & Migration,* which are available at a substantial discount to members. The scientific results of important surveys, like the recently completed *The New Atlas of the Breeding Birds in Britain and Ireland: 1988–1991,* appear in book form and members can often benefit from substantial pre–publication discounts. Please send an SAE to the Membership Secretary, BTO, The National Centre for Ornithology, The Nunnery, Thetford, Norfolk IP24 2PU for information about membership.

## Nest boxing and conservation

Many people purchase and erect nest boxes in their garden. Sadly, some of the designs currently available are unsuitable or positively dangerous. This book will enable you to make a sensible choice and, much more usefully, it illustrates the full range of nest box designs that you can use to cater for a wide range of our native birds.

Mankind has modified the natural environment in Britain. Even an apparently ideal stretch of woodland may be carefully managed for timber production. Land managers may remove dead and diseased trees every winter so that there are no holes for birds to nest in. In such cases small tit nest boxes will enable their numbers to build up. Tree Sparrows may form a colony and, if you are within the range of Pied Flycatchers, you may be able to encourage these attractive migrants to become the dominant breeding bird. Beyond these small birds, which will take to a standard small nest box, the book contains specialist designs for Tawny Owls, Redstarts, Stock Doves, Starlings, Kestrels, Treecreepers, Jackdaws and other woodland species. If apparently wild areas, such as woodland, need boxes for a range of species to be able to breed, imagine how much you can do in your own garden. This book gives advice not just for special boxes, like those on the house for Swifts or House Martins, but also for modifying the habitat to encourage other open nesting species. You can find details in these pages on the provision of stick bundles, nest bases and, of course, providing safe sites not vulnerable to cat or Magpie predation.

## Keeping up the good work

Much of the information within this book has accrued over more than 50 years of data gathering through the Nest Record Scheme. This is one of the simplest and most important of the permanent surveys run by the BTO. All you need to do is to regularly visit active nests of wild birds and record their progress on a specially designed card. The scheme enables the BTO to monitor the changing timing and success of our nesting birds. This provides a vital part of the Integrated Population Monitoring Scheme. We have designed this major BTO initiative to allow us to untangle natural changes in breeding success from those population changes induced by mankind.

Whilst the BTO hopes that most nest recorders will be members, the scheme is also open to those who have not yet joined. If you can report from as few as half a dozen nests of common garden species each year, you will be making a really useful contribution to this survey. The emphasis is on careful and accurate observation. You do not have to be an expert bird identifier provided you can be sure of the identity of each nest for which you complete a card. If you would like a starter pack, which includes instructions and a handful of cards, write to the Nest Record Unit at BTO HQ.

By joining the BTO you will become a better birder. You will be more closely involved with the birds you watch. For a modest annual membership fee, the other benefits include:

- discounts from books and sound recordings on joining
- pre-publication book offers
- free use of our library
- six copies of *BTO News* a year
- your own local contact as part of our Regional Network
- reduced subscriptions to the BTO's journals *Bird Study* and *Ringing & Migration*

- occasional local meetings and newsletters
- the opportunity to take part in a variety of surveys
- helpful advice and information from BTO staff
- training courses in ringing and census techniques
- the knowledge that your subscription is helping Britain's birds and their habitats.

To join, send an SAE to: The Membership Secretary, BTO, The National Centre for Ornithology, The Nunnery, Thetford, Norfolk IP24 2PU or you can telephone on 0842 750050 or fax on 0842 750030

*The Nest Record Scheme is carried out under contract from the Joint Nature Conservation Committee, on behalf of English Nature, Scottish National Heritage and the Countryside Council for Wales, and under a contract from the Department of the Environment for Northern Ireland.*